Self Build

Design and build your own home

RIBA Enterprises

Self Build: design and build your own home
Julian Owen

© Julian Owen, 2004

Published by RIBA Enterprises Ltd, 15 Bonhill Street, London EC2P 2EA

ISBN 1 85946 139 5

Product Code 36159

British Library Cataloguing in Publications Data
A catalogue record for this book is available from the British Library

Publisher: Steven Cross
Commissioning Editor: Matthew Thompson
Editor: Ian McDonald
Project Editor: Anna Walters
Designed by: US2 Design
Printed and bound by: Latimer Trend & Company Ltd, Plymouth

Dedication

To Jill, Katy and Sophie.

About The Author

Julian Owen MBE RIBA is an architect who has been helping people build and improve their homes for many years. He has written magazine articles and regularly delivered seminars at exhibitions on the subject of improving, designing and constructing homes. He runs his own practice in the East Midlands, and is currently chair of ASBA, the architects' network that he founded with his colleague, Adrian Spawforth in 1993. He can be contacted through his website: www.julianowen.co.uk.

Throughout the book symbols are used to draw the readers' attention to important points.

 Hot tips give useful information and 'tricks of the trade'.

 Watchpoints draw attention to important aspects that are sometimes overlooked, or warn of pitfalls.

Self Build:
Design and Build Your Own Home

Acknowledgements

Particular thanks are due to the following for supplying images:

Magazines

Homebuilding and Renovating, 01527 834400

Self Build and Design, 01283 742970

Architects

11.04 Architects, London, 020 7739 2121

Building Design Architects, East Sussex, 01323 410095

Cleveland Architectural Design, Stockton-on-Tees, 01642 888050

David Randell Architects, Devon, 01884 254465

David Thorp, Birmingham, 0121 777 5925

Eades Hotwani, Hertfordshire, 01462 455257

Four Square Design Ltd, Berkshire, 01488 71384

Garside Architect, Lancashire, 01706 642992

JDW Architects, Monmouthshire, 01873 851125

Julian Owen Associates, East Midlands, 0115 922 9831

Mole Architects, Cambridgeshire, 01353 688287

Peter Knowles Architect, Derbyshire, 01629 636362

Reed Architects, Welsh Marches, 01544 260523

Steven Buttler Chartered Architect, Cumbria, 01228 546487

Thomas Associates, Lancashire, 01524 381555

Walter Wood Associates, Edinburgh, 0131 319 1260

Suppliers/Manufacturers

Ramowski Clarke, land surveyors, 0115 928 9091

Beco Products Ltd, suppliers of permanently insulated formwork systems, 01652 651641

H & H Celcon, suppliers of concrete blocks and the Jamera concrete building system, 01732 886333

Huf Haus, suppliers and erectors of modern-style timber frame buildings, 0870 2000 035

Velux Company Ltd, suppliers of roof windows, 0870 166 7676

York Handmade Brick Co. Ltd, suppliers of handmade bricks, 01347 838881

This book was inspired by Adrian Spawforth, a fellow architect and co-founder of ASBA. I would also like to thank Richard Owen for his work as an unofficial editor, David Snell for his advice, friendship and general guidance over the last few years, and the members and directors of the ASBA Architects' Network for all their support and contributions. Jason Orme of *Homebuilding and Renovating* Magazine and Ross Stokes of *Self Build and Design* Magazine have played a crucial role helping me obtain many of the photographs, for which I am grateful.

Foreword

There can be no doubt that the British public is becoming ever more design and style conscious – and nowhere is this more true than in the home. Marry this with the British obsession with homeownership and you have the recipe for the phenomenon that is self-build. Only a few years ago, self-build was still widely seen as an activity exclusively for the DIY fanatic willing to spend a few years living in a caravan on a muddy building site. Today you can hardly turn on a television or read a newspaper without reading about self-build and it seems that almost everyone has an idea of what their dream home would be like, should they ever get the chance to build it.

Property makeover shows have taught us all how to transform our existing living space and increasingly how to adapt and alter the layout. Ultimately, however, the constraints and limitations of our aging and outdated housing stock leads to the gradual realisation that the only way to achieve what we want without serious compromise, is to build from scratch.

Testament to the growth in individual homebuilding is the success of *Homebuilding & Renovating magazine*, of which I have been editor for ten years. Copy sales have increased more than fourfold since 1994 and the magazine now sells over 40,000 copies a month and is the best selling self-build magazine in the UK.

Self Build: design and build your own home has been brilliantly conceived to convince the would-be home builder that high quality self build is perfectly within their reach. Its author, Julian Owen, is an experienced architect who has worked with self-builders for over 13 years and knows better than most that good design does not need to be compromised by more pragmatic but equally important concerns. Indeed, over the years he has built up a successful practice designing and managing the building of custom-made self build homes all over the country. He is a founding member of ASBA, Associated Self Build Architects, an affiliation of architects specialising in helping people to build their own homes, speaks regularly at shows and seminars, and in 2003 he was awarded an MBE for services to architecture.

Part of his mission is to dispel the myth that self build or renovation has to mean rolling up your sleeves and getting up-close and personal with a cement mixer. Another part of it is to prove the maxim that if you can afford to buy an existing house in a particular location, you can afford to build an equivalent but better home in the same location. *Self Build: design and build your own home* more than demonstrates these lessons. Its information is laid out in straightforward step-by-step sections, written in a direct and easy-to-read style that belies the complexity of the subject, and the content is packed full of the insights, advice and warnings of someone who has seen it all.

There are plenty of information resources for anyone thinking of self building or renovating but none to date has given design quality quite such a high billing. Published by the Royal Institute of British Architects' publishing arm, I am very pleased to be able to recommend this important new addition to the literature for all those self builders who believe that good design can unlock the potential of great living.

Michael Holmes
Editor, *Homebuilding and Renovating* magazine

Self Build:

Design and Build Your Own Home

Self Build:

Design and Build Your Own Home

Making the Decision

Surveys have consistently shown that the vast majority of the UK population would very much like to have a house designed and built to their own specifications. In spite of this enthusiasm, only around 15,000 to 20,000 families a year actually manage to build their own homes. This is a significant number in housing terms: more than any single house developer, and maybe 10 per cent of all houses built each year. But it is probably nowhere near the number who would actually do it, if they knew it was an option available to them. This book is written as a guide for anyone who would like to know how self build can be achieved, and as a manual for people to actually start the process. It is arranged broadly in sequence to provide information, hints and advice related to each stage in the project. The format is based on the standard job stages that architects use when running any kind of building project. It gives the necessary information in as concise a way as possible, and many of the checklists are designed to be copied and used as part of the management of a project.

The Design and Construction Process

This book is set out to follow broadly the design and construction of an individual house. There are several paths along the way, depending on which choices you make. The timeline is based on a typical progression, where an architect is used to complete a design and then a main contractor builds the house. The variations to the theme are discussed later in the book, but the process is broadly the same, with mainly the responsibilities changing.

Some Frequently Asked Questions

I don't want to do the building work myself. Am I a 'self builder'?

As far as many people are concerned, you are. This title used to be applied only to those who actually carry out a significant portion of the construction work themselves. Unfortunately, no-one has come with a snappy term for those who get a professional builder to do the work on their behalf. As a result, the term is now used as shorthand for anyone who arranges the design and construction of their own home. This causes a lot of confusion, but for the moment it remains the only term in common usage. If you feel the description should not apply to you, be comforted by the fact that even the Duke and Duchess of York count as 'self builders'.

Why Do It?

The are many good reasons. Saving money is often the major one since, if a project goes well and the tax advantages are used to their full benefit, it is possible to save tens of thousands of pounds. However, the reason most consistently given is that it offers the opportunity to customise a home to suit the individual tastes and requirements of a family. A general dissatisfaction with the newly built houses on the market in the UK is also a prime motivation.

Why Should You Do It?

- strong desire to create an individual home
- cheaper than buying new (if well managed)
- a jump up the 'housing ladder'
- enthusiasm for DIY
- dissatisfaction with newly built housing estates
- desire to live in an eco-friendly house
- an individual home is a status symbol

Can I afford it?

If you can afford a detached house in the area where you want to build, assuming that you can find a site, you can afford to build your own home.

Am I the sort of person who can do this?

People from all walks of life get their own house designed and built. Some formal management skills are useful, but many full-time mothers have proved very adept at dealing with planners, architects and builders – raising children probably gives you a grounding in all the skills you need to do this! Personal qualities are far more important than knowledge of the building industry, or even a track record of DIY projects. You can get expert help at almost every step way of the way, and it is entirely up to you how much input you have. Many couples successfully divide responsibilities between them. For example, one leading on the design side and the other dealing with financial management.

How long will it take?

The average interval from finding a site to moving in is about a year, if you use a professional builder to do the work. The time needed before this to find a site is difficult to quantify, since it can vary considerably. Some people inherit or are given a plot, others spend many years looking before they find the right spot for their dream home. If you decide to do all the building work yourself, the build programme is likely to be much longer – possibly more than a year.

If it's so great, why isn't everyone doing it?

There are many reasons why there are fewer of these sort of projects than there could be. A major one is that although there is plenty of building land around, most of it is only available in large amounts. For example, it is easier in the UK to get planning permission for a huge housing estate in the green belt, than it is for a single house. Another reason is cultural: unlike the Scandinavians, or North Americans, we have been brought up to believe that, in housing terms, we must make the best of what we are given. This arrangement suits politicians, planners and developers very well. The only people who lose out are the customers.

Where can I find out more?

Because this is a thriving and expanding market, there are some excellent sources of reference easily available in the form of books and magazines. There are many exhibitions which are regularly staged across the UK, and even a permanent self-build centre.

Magazines

Homebuilding and Renovating
A good quality publication that deals with all kinds of domestic building projects, including one-off houses.

Build It
The oldest magazine for self builders, with lots of case studies and practical advice.

Self Build and Design
A good source of ideas, in design terms as well as more practical matters.

Grand Designs
A tie-in with the Channel Four TV series, very design-orientated.

Books

Building Your Own Home
One of the first books to tackle the subject comprehensively, this book gives a thorough grounding in the whole process from start to finish.

The Housebuilder's Bible
This covers many of the practical issues, with detailed and updated guidance on building costs.

All About Self Build
A comprehensive, highly detailed guide to self build.

Exhibitions

The National Homebuilding and Renovating Exhibition, NEC Birmingham
This is held annually, usually in March.

Regional Homebuilding and Renovating Exhibitions
These are held throughout the year, in places such as London, Glasgow, Shepton Mallet and Harrogate.

Interbuild
Held every two years, this huge exhibition is designed for the whole construction industry and can be a bit daunting – but every kind of product, service and supplier are there.

Television

'Grand Designs' is a regular series on Channel Four, which takes an hour-long episode to cover each project.

Key People

You will have to deal with a range of individuals, officials and professionals to get your house designed and built. Here are just a few of them:

Estate Agent
Will probably act on behalf of the vendor when you purchase the plot. May also value the plot for you and your building society.

Solicitor
Will carry out conveyancing for the plot purchase and assist with legal restrictions, like covenants etc.

Building Society Manager/Finance Provider Representative
You will probably need financial help, and you need someone familiar with the particular needs of your project.

Architect
Can be used for finding and assessing a site, designing the house, preparing local authority applications and managing the contractor on site.

Kit Sales Representative
Helps you to choose and order a kit house.

Planning Officer
The final decision on a planning application will be made by the senior planners or the planning committee, but a planning officer can advise on what is likely to be approved and what may be refused.

Planning Consultant

If you have a controversial application, or wish to appeal against a refusal, a planning consultant is trained in planning law and can improve your chances of success.

Structural Engineer

Most buildings require structural details and calculations that need to be prepared by an engineer.

Quantity Surveyor

A QS can prepare budget estimates at planning stage, and detailed quantities for contractors to price from. They are most effective on larger projects.

Building Control Officer

An application for approval under the Building Regulations is separate from the planning approval process. The Building Control Officer approves the application and inspects the work on site.

Landscape Designer/Contractor

If your external works are extensive, you may need a specialist.

Party Wall Surveyor

If your house is built close to a neighbour's foundations and certain conditions apply, you are obliged by law to serve a Party Wall Notice on them. If the notice is challenged, party wall surveyors must be appointed to resolve the issue.

Contract Manager/Foreman

In the case of a small company, the managerial role and the site supervision are carried out by the same person. Larger companies tend to split the responsibility between a contract manager (for the former task) and a site foreman (for the latter).

Subcontractor/Tradesman

Strictly speaking, a subcontractor is employed by a building contractor, but the term is often used to describe anyone with a specialised skill or trade.

Supplier/Manufacturer

If you are personally specifying products, you will want to deal directly with the suppliers. Most are happy to provide literature, samples and advice.

Builders' Merchant

Even if you don't plan to order any materials yourself, these are good places to see samples of products and materials, and to gain valuable advice on using them.

Accountant

Given the size of the investment, an accountant can provide valuable advice on how to maximise the tax benefits available, which include avoiding VAT and Capital Gains Tax.

Project Preparation

Having made the decision that you would like to go ahead with the project, what are the first active steps you should take to reach your goal? First, before anything else, you must work out how much you can afford, and what you should be able to get for your money. If you skip or gloss over this stage there is a real risk that you will suffer disappointment further along the way. At the same time, you can start to examine what you want to get out of the house, and build up a picture of how it should look. Keep a careful record of anything that you decide or any information that you collect – it will come in very handy later on.

Summary of This Stage:
- Preparing a Budget
- Obtaining Finance
- Dealing with the Taxman
- Procurement Route
- Preparing a Brief
- Finding a Site

Preparing a Budget

Before you make a proper start on the journey to the design and construction of your own home, you need a clear idea of what you are working towards. For most people the map, guide and point of reference is their budget calculation. At the early stages, these calculations will all be 'best guesses', but you should review them at every key point in the process. As you progress, the figures will become more accurate as you add to your knowledge and start to get a clearer idea of actual costs. The current budget calculations should be at the forefront of your mind whenever you have a key decision to make. There is no doubt that many building projects run into difficulties when the actual costs are discovered, and there is no magic formula that can guarantee you will not go over budget. But you can do a lot to reduce the risk of this happening.

Into the unknown

If anyone starts to tell you, in the early stages of the project, how much it is going to cost to build your house, stop them. Find someone who is wise enough to tell you the truth – which is that they don't know. At this point, you do not know how much the site is going to cost, or what level of specification you will use, or what will happen to UK construction costs over the next 12 months. You don't know the answers to the many questions which will influence how much you will end up paying. All kinds of people quote all sorts of figures, particularly if they are trying to sell you something. If the figures being quoted seem very low, be suspicious, because there are no easy bargains in the development business and you really do get what you pay for. There are a few costs that you cannot influence, like taxes, and you will just have to accept them. But most are in your control, to a greater or lesser extent. The biggest single influence on the price of your home is you – how you run the project and the choices that you make as you do it. To set a budget, you need to pick a realistic target figure, and then aim for it. Check it regularly as you go along, and adjust what you do next accordingly.

Where Will the Money Go?

There are some rules of thumb that are often quoted to help people work out their budget at the beginning, such as that the land should cost about one third of your budget (or a half or more, if you live in a land-starved area like the Southeast of England). Another useful figure at this stage is an estimate of cost per square foot, or square metre. But there is already a trap here for the unwary, who may then make the following sort of calculation:

Total Budget	= £200,000
Cost of land	= £60,000
Remainder for build	= £140,000
£140,000 divided by, say, £80/sq ft	= a house of 1,750 sq ft.

This calculation, although often encouraged by many, is a dangerous one to use without being aware of its limitations. Table 1, below, which lists all the incidental costs, as well as the obvious ones, can be used, even at an early stage, to estimate a more realistic budget. If you recalculate the budget allowing for all these things, the actual amount available to build with is more likely to be a little over half your budget, and suddenly your notional house is several hundred square feet smaller.

This misunderstanding is an important cause of many people abandoning the dream, as they realise, contrary to their first impression, that there is not a large profit to be easily made. Hopefully they find this out before they have bought their site and started to build.

Developer v house builder costs

Massive profits are occasionally made by the lucky self-build few, although often their story ignores the effect of rampant house-price inflation, which can make it hard to lose money. But you have a built-in advantage over the main competition, the small house-development company: you are spared many of the costs that the latter incur.

You can also create further advantages for yourself by being more creative with the design, and taking on plots with unusual or difficult constraints that the professionals will not want to waste time and resources on. Your other natural advantage is probably well known to anyone who is moved to read a book like this. Most commercially developed housing is designed for estate agents, that is, most of the design requirements are dictated by agents who will calculate how to appeal to the biggest market possible for a given type of development. Their credo – which includes the idea that the value of the house is higher if you maximise the number of bedrooms, however small they end up – is self-fulfilling, since they all give the same advice. Houses which have been built by individuals do not necessarily follow these rules, which gives them a rarity value, provided they have been well designed.

Building costs

When drawing up a budget, you have to make a good guess at how much the building work will be, and the only way of doing this is to assume a price per square foot (or metre). There are many ways of working this figure out, such as asking professionals who know the area you are going to build in, or consulting the specialist magazines, which supply this kind of information.

If you use magazines to estimate your building cost, do not rely only on the figures quoted in articles – these may not include incidental costs, and proud self builders naturally add a bit of 'spin' for the press. Some publications include cost indexes, which are more objective, at the back, but don't rely on them – get opinions from local professionals as well.

Table 1: Budget Planner - Typical Expenses		
Item	**Your Cost**	
Site Stage		
Site Investigations, e.g. ground conditions		May not be required – can cost several thousands of pounds.
Land Cost		Typically anything from $\frac{1}{4}$ to $\frac{1}{2}$ of your total budget.
Solicitor's Fees		
Stamp Duty		1% for land value between £60,000 and £250,000 (applicable in 2004).
Public Liability Insurance		To cover accidents before building work starts.
Site Security and Clearance Costs		To make the site safe. Some sites will need little or nothing.
Measured Survey of Site		Essential, except for the simplest sites.
Finance arrangement costs		Mortgage application, etc.
Professional Fees		
Architect's Fees		Could be a percentage or an hourly rate.
Engineer's Fees		Usually an hourly rate.
Quantity Surveyor's Fees		Budget costing by a QS at this stage can be useful.
Planning Fees		£220 in 2004. No VAT charged.
Planning Appeal (if required)		Potentially expensive, if a planning consultant is necessary.
Detailed Design		
Building Regulations Drawings Package		
Building Regulations Local Authority Fee		Typically £150–£200. VAT is charged. If over a 300 sq m-size threshold, the fee is higher.
Tender package preparation		
Printing and Postage Costs		Can be several hundred pounds if it is a big house, and tenders are sent to 5 or 6 contractors.
Site Costs		
Accommodation during construction		Could be rental, extra mortgage costs, or mobile-home hire.
Building Regulations Inspection Fee		£250–£300. If over a 300 sq m size threshold, the fee is higher.
Service connections – water, gas, electricity supply and drainage		Cost can vary enormously, from a few hundred pounds to many thousands.
Contingencies		Minimum of 5% of build cost. Usually spent on something in the end.
Certification		By building warranty/guarantee provider or architect.
Contract Management		On-site service provided by an architect (or other, suitably qualified, professional).
Employer's Liability Insurance, Contractor Insurance		Only if you self manage or choose DIY route – otherwise, should be main contractor's responsibility.
House Construction		Estimate a cost/sq m early in the budget-planning stage.
External works		May be essential, e.g. new road access, or driveway.
Kitchen Fittings		Usually a separate element of the construction.
Moving House		
New Furniture and Equipment		Most people want this, to go with their new house.
Removal Costs		

To add to the confusion, different organisations and professionals work out the floor area of a house in different ways. An estate agent tends to indicate the useable area of a house, which means that each room size is measured and added to a total. A quantity surveyor is interested in the building materials, so will probably measure the area of a house around the line of the outside wall. Someone selling a kit house will tend to quote area in the same way as the QS, because it makes the house sound bigger. The same house can appear to be 10–20 per cent larger, depending on the method of calculation.

As well as differences in how the area of a final building may be measured, what is included in each square foot can also vary. For example, most figures quoted make allowance for windows, decorations, sanitary goods, etc., but some do not. So, as soon as you try to use 'per square foot' prices to examine costs in detail – for example to compare relative costs of different rooms, or to decide how much an extra 5 sq ft will cost to add to your house – this method becomes hopelessly unreliable. Prices quoted by professionals or kit suppliers may not include the whole cost of the completed building, so make sure you get them to state exactly what they are talking about.

Since your budget is a target, rather than a prediction, you should pick a figure that is realistic, and accept that you will have to trim your requirements to suit what you will be able to afford. If you can do this early on, the chances of keeping within your budget are greatly increased. But, however careful you try to be, picking a cost per square foot price to aim for is an art, not a science.

Table 2: Building Cost Ready Reckoner

All sizes (but not costs) are for typical houses. Prices are average for UK in 2004

Imperial

Typical House Type	Floor Area	Build Cost				
		Budget	Average	Good	High	Very High
Build cost £/sq ft		£50	£65	£80	£100	£120
Very Small Bungalow	750	£37,500	£48,750	£60,000	£75,000	£90,000
Small 3-bed semi	850	£42,500	£55,250	£68,000	£85,000	£102,000
Medium 3-bed	1150	£57,500	£74,750	£92,000	£115,000	£138,000
Average 4-bed	1400	£70,000	£91,000	£112,000	£140,000	£168,000
Good sized 4-bed/small 5-bed	1600	£80,000	£104,000	£128,000	£160,000	£192,000
Average 5-bed	1800	£90,000	£117,000	£144,000	£180,000	£216,000
Large 5-Bed	2000	£100,000	£130,000	£160,000	£200,000	£240,000

Metric - Figures are different because they have been rounded up

Typical House Type	Floor Area	Build Cost				
		Budget	Average	Good	High	Very High
Build cost £/sq m		£540	£700	£860	£1,075	£1,290
Very Small Bungalow	70	£37,800	£49,000	£60,200	£75,250	£90,300
Small 3-bed semi	79	£42,660	£55,300	£67,940	£84,925	£101,910
Medium 3-bed	106	£57,240	£74,200	£91,160	£113,950	£136,740
Average 4-bed	130	£70,200	£91,000	£111,800	£139,750	£167,700
Good sized 4-bed/small 5-bed	150	£81,000	£105,000	£129,000	£161,250	£193,500
Average 5-bed	168	£90,720	£117,600	£144,480	£180,600	£216,720
Large 5-Bed	186	£100,440	£130,200	£159,960	£199,950	£239,940

What will Affect the Cost of Your House?

House size v quality of specification

The bigger the house and the better the quality of materials and fittings, the more it is likely to cost. Both these parameters are in your control, and should be the subject of careful thought and examination. If you assume minimum quality, to get the biggest house, you are likely to be disappointed, because most people would not be happy with this standard. It is likely that you will want to upgrade as the project progresses and, consequently, may go over budget.

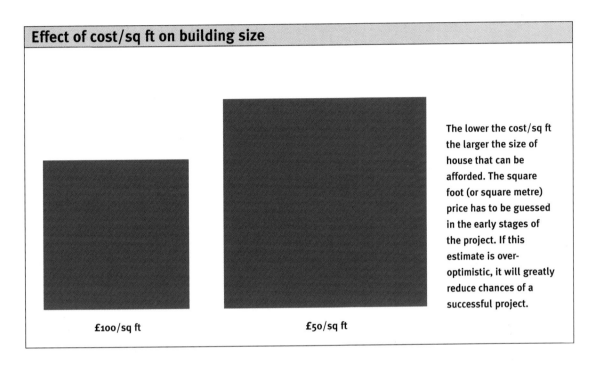

Effect of cost/sq ft on building size

£100/sq ft

£50/sq ft

The lower the cost/sq ft the larger the size of house that can be afforded. The square foot (or square metre) price has to be guessed in the early stages of the project. If this estimate is over-optimistic, it will greatly reduce chances of a successful project.

Where you build

The most expensive place in the UK to build a house is London, followed by the rest of the Southeast. The difference between there and cheaper areas, such as Yorkshire and Wales can be 10-15 per cent or more. This reflects things that vary across the country in a similar way, such as wages and the general cost of living. However these figures are only generally true, and local conditions also come into play: for example, building on a Scottish island could be very expensive because there may be only one builder, who has a monopoly. If you are in a neighbourhood which is known to be wealthy, some of the companies you deal with may apply an unwritten rule and load their prices accordingly.

Your input

How much work you do yourself will obviously affect how much your project costs in hard cash. But, whether you get involved in the work or not, you should account for the cost of your own time. This is an essential consideration if you are self-employed, or can earn overtime. Of course, for many people, the satisfaction of doing something themselves is a reward in itself. But there is no point in doing work that you do not enjoy, if you could earn more elsewhere than it would cost to pay someone to do it. Likewise, if you take a long time to do a particular task, or are not very good at it, it will help your budget more if you use a professional for that portion of the works.

Site conditions and constraints

There is a section on this later in the book. But, unless you calculate the extra costs of a tricky site before you buy and then deduct them from the asking price, they can have a big effect on your budget. You must find out as much as possible about the site, and check the effect on your budget, before you commit yourself. Conversely, many people have enhanced their profits by a bit of lateral thinking and making good use of an apparently awkward site.

Cost-effective v cheap

Be aware of the difference between these two concepts. For example, a cheap material may lose you money later in maintenance costs. It will be a false economy if you end up with an unsatisfactory end result, or could get a much better product for a small extra outlay.

Finance costs

How you arrange you finances, how good a deal you get, and how interest rates fluctuate will all affect your budget.

Management

How well you manage your project will be crucial to keeping on budget. See 'How to Keep on Budget', below.

Building for profit or for a better life?

Many families start with idea that their house will be a money-making venture but end up building their dream home, without much in the way of profit materialising. This is fine, as long as the decision is taken deliberately along the way. It is almost impossible for the average person to totally detach themselves from the process and make the hard-nosed decisions that developers do throughout a project. If you are building speculatively, you only spend money where it will help get a better sale price, and you have to avoid personalising the design too much. If, like most, you are trying to steer a middle course between personalising the house and building an investment, be aware that this is a problem. Don't start spending disproportionately on aspects of the house that will not necessarily improve saleability.

How to Keep on Budget

With any one-off project, there can be no absolute certainty of price. The people who do best financially are usually the ones who manage the risks most effectively.

Be realistic, get realistic advice

The biggest problem you face in trying to control the budget is your natural optimism – few pessimists ever embark on a project such as this. Salespeople, pundits and professionals who suggest that you will become rich will probably sound attractive and convincing. You will want to believe that everything will be easy, and that you will end up with a substantial addition to your bank account. In short, a part of you wants to be lied to. Get lots of advice, read up as much as possible and then be brutally honest with yourself. Don't work to the most favourable figures you can find, but pick realistic ones. With a bit of luck, you may do very well financially (some genuinely do make 30 per cent or more), but count this as a bonus, and keep your expectations realistic.

Monitor and discuss

Constantly revisit your budget, and keep doing this until the house is finished. Discuss it regularly with your family and professional advisors. Update it, and replace your assumptions with real figures as you go along.

Control small decisions

It is quite rare for a single, big decision to be made that unexpectedly drives up costs. If you decide that the bath taps must be gold-plated, or that you need an extra room, you will probably guess that it will cost more money. The usual reason that costs go up is because a series of small decisions are made, each of which, on their own, have a negligible effect on the total cost, but which collectively result in tender prices coming in way over budget. These items then have to be taken out of the contract to reduce the cost again. Be aware of this phenomenon, and try to avoid it.

Contingency

It cannot be stressed enough how important it is to have some financial reserves, for unexpected costs. At the very start of a typical project this amount should be 10 per cent of the total budget. As building work is about to start, it should be at least 5 per cent. This money will be spent, even if it is on a nicer kitchen or a statue for the garden.

Professional team

Pick your team with care. If you are sufficiently self-aware, identify your weaknesses and make sure that you get help to cover them. A good builder or architect will easily pay for themselves in money saved, quality achieved, and stress relieved. A builder who is honest, reliable and efficient, but more expensive, will usually be cheaper by the end of the project than another who quotes a very low price initially and has none of these qualities.

Good design

Design is not just about how things look. A well-planned design will get the best end result for your money. Good design will also ensure that problems are anticipated and 'designed-out' where possible, allowing you to save money, or spend it on other aspects of the building.

Preparation, preparation, preparation

You cannot be too well-prepared for building work to start. The more that has been worked out in advance, the fewer extras there will be

Tender correctly

The rules for obtaining prices are covered later in this book. If this crucial stage is not managed properly, the budget can go awry as building work progresses. If you choose not to get accurate tendered prices for the build, you will probably have to pay more for the luxury. If there is only one builder or supplier that you want for something, at least give them the impression that you are getting other prices.

Changes of mind

If you change something after you have had competitive prices, it will be a bit more expensive. If you change your mind after something has been built, it will be a lot more expensive. If you are unsure about some aspect of the design, you can ask for two options to be priced as part of the tenders. If it is a fitting or component, you can exclude it from the contract, and give yourself the option of getting it from somewhere else. If you are really unsure, identify it as an item that may be changed, and get the builder to check with you before it is ordered or built.

Temporary accommodation costs

Don't forget to include these in your calculations, and allow for the project overrunning.

Check site thoroughly

Investigate the plot as much as possible before you buy it. See the section on 'Site Investigation', later on in this book, for full details.

Never pay in advance

This cannot be strictly applied in reality, because there may be some specialist components that are manufactured particularly for your project, and which will require a deposit of some kind. Also, many kit suppliers insist on a downpayment. Otherwise, pay promptly, pay in stages if appropriate, but pay after the service or product has been provided.

Time is money

Try to keep the project on programme, especially after you have paid for the land, the first big outlay. Even if you are not paying interest, you will be losing it from your deposit account or investment portfolio by having money tied up.

Keep good records

If there are arguments about money, such as who should pay what, or you want to get the best rebate from the taxman possible, some well-kept contemporaneous notes, or carefully saved receipts, should help you to win the argument.

Obtaining Finance

Most people will need the help of a money-lend institution to be able to start their self-build project. In the past, arranging finance was a major barrier preventing people from building their own homes; self builders were seen as high-risk. Banks and building societies now recognise that they are actually good customers, and that this is a lucrative market. Most of them offer special deals, which take into account the particular financial needs that arise. One very positive effect of involvement with a company that understands the design and construction process is that they will check that you are going the right way about your project before they agree to lend.

Do You Qualify?

Apart from the usual conditions that apply when you ask for a loan to buy a house, there are some extra criteria that you will have to satisfy. The house must be your own private dwelling, and not for commercial use or part of a property-development business. Lenders will also expect some form of current planning approval to be in place on the site (with a few years to run), and will expect a certificate at the end to demonstrate that the house has been well built. If you can satisfy these requirements, and demonstrate that you are approaching the project in an organised and thorough fashion, you should have no problem obtaining a loan.

Getting the Best Out of Your Mortgage

1. Talk to potential mortgage providers before you draw up your budget and start looking for a site.
2. Prepare a budget, and show that you are at least trying to minimise risks.
3. Prepare a cash-flow forecast and try to reduce the amount you borrow early on.
4. Shop around. Talk to specialist brokers, and make your own enquiries.
5. Get details of what amount will be released at what stage, and compare them.
6. Make sure that the deal is flexible enough to accommodate your project, e.g. check when stage payments are made.
7. Never borrow up to your absolute limit. You may need to get more money in an emergency.

Stage Payments

Because a building project incurs costs progressively over time, you do not need all the money in one go at the start. You may need help with the land purchase, then there will be a wait whilst you get organised, then you will need a series of payments as work progresses. You will probably not be able to get a loan for 100 per cent of the land cost, and the maximum you are likely to get for the building work is 95 per cent. You may need to have as much as 50 per cent of the land cost available from your own funds.

> *The money released by the building society or bank will be based on their own calculations, not on your actual costs. Prepare a cash-flow forecast before work commences, and check that you will be able to cover bills as they arise.*

What to Check When Investigating a Mortgage

- What percentage of the value does the mortgage provider lend for land (if any), and how much for construction?
- What kind of certification will they accept (e.g. architect's, insurer's)?
- What are their charges and interest rates?
- Is there a local contact who understands one-off house projects? Sometimes the only expertise and knowledge is all at head office.
- Do they insist on full planning permission (i.e. a detailed design) before they will release any money?
- At what stages will they release money, and what amounts (typically 4 stages – the amounts vary considerably)?
- When do you start repaying (e.g. as project proceeds)?
- Are there any hidden charges?
- How can they help if you wish to remain in your current home until building work is complete?
- What inspections of their own will they undertake, and what will they charge you for them?
- Will they insist on a professional builder, or allow you to do some or all of the work yourself?

Dealing With the Taxman

Wherever there is money being spent or made (legally) there are taxes to be paid. In some ways, the taxman is pretty kind to self builders. If relatively large sums of money are involved, it is worth getting some professional advice from an accountant early on in the proceedings, or even consulting a specialist, such as a VAT advisor. How you approach your project, and how it is presented to the tax collectors, can affect how much you have to pay.

VAT

If you are building a private house in the UK, you can either ask the builder to zero-rate all relevant invoices, or claim the VAT back at the end if you are using several contractors. The building must be used for residential purposes, so if you are planning to build a house that incorporates a business, this may not apply. But if you are only going to use one or two rooms to work from home, it will be treated as a dwelling.

The VAT rule applies to anything that is ordinarily incorporated into the building. For anything that falls outside this description, VAT will have to be paid. Unfortunately, HM Customs and Excise have some fairly obscure rules about what constitutes a part of the house, and what does not. If you are using a single contractor, who is going to buy most of the materials for you, it is fairly simple, and they should make you aware of which items will require VAT paying.

But if you are self managing, or building for yourself, you will have to keep careful records, and be aware of what you can claim back. It is vital to get a proper VAT receipt – one which is fully itemised, has your name on it and has the vendor's VAT registration number. At the end of the project – the VAT people say within 3 months of completing the house, but don't define 'completion' particularly well – you have one opportunity to claim the VAT you have paid back. So it is best to leave it as late as is reasonable.

HM Customs and Excise have a helpline service, and also issue a free booklet that goes into some detail on how the rules are applied, which is well worth getting (it is called 'VAT refunds for "Do it yourself" builders and converters').

Make sure you get a Completion Certificate from the building control officer, and keep it safe. Customs and Excise will accept it as the date of completion, if it suits you to produce it.

Table 3: Saving or Claiming Back VAT - Some Examples	
Can Avoid or Reclaim VAT	**Cannot Reclaim VAT**
Alarm systems	Professional and local authority Fees
Fitted kitchen	Most fitted furniture
Ventilation extracts	Kitchen appliances
Some soft landscaping	Carpets
Vinyl floor covering	Sheds, ponds, garden ornaments, tennis courts
Garage doors	Automatic garage-door-opening systems
	Plant hire

Capital Gains Tax

This tax is levied on the appreciation of an asset, i.e. the difference between what you bought it for and what it is worth when you sell. However, if you make a profit when you sell your family home (they call it your 'principal private residence'), you do not incur Capital Gains Tax. There are also some exemptions for people who build a new house for themselves whilst remaining in their existing home. After you have moved into your new house, you can nominate it as your principal private residence, and sell your own home without paying CGT. There are some time limits stated in the legislation, which is complex. The point of the rules is to prevent people from earning an income by simply moving house constantly, and avoiding paying tax on what is really a development business. As long as you are not doing this, your build programme does not become over-extended (more than a couple of years), and you have not owned the land for a long time before building on it, you should not fall foul of these rules. If in any doubt, get advice from a tax specialist.

Council Tax

Each local authority sets its own level of council tax, which is chargeable on properties that are considered to be suitable for occupation. If you don't live in the house, or furnish it, you will have a few months' grace after it is finished, so you avoid having to pay tax for two properties at once.

If you use a mobile home on the site, you may have to pay council tax on it if you live in it all or some of the time.

Stamp Duty

Building your own home is a way of reducing or avoiding stamp duty, since you only pay it on the land. For example: in 2004, if a plot of land is worth £60,000 or less there is no stamp duty. Between £60,000 and £250,000 it is 1 per cent. It then increases in similar steps with the land value.

Preparing a Brief

When you finally reach the point at which you and your architect start to develop a design for a house, make sure that it is your home that you are going to end up with, that suits your needs and aspirations, and not just a house. To pull off this trick successfully, you should start investigating as soon as possible what the dwelling will need to be like. All self builders do this to some extent, before they reach the point of realising their dream. If a well-thought-out brief is developed before the site is acquired, you will be far better prepared to get on with the exciting job of designing the house.

The stage after you have decided to actively pursue the project but before you have found a site can be a frustrating time, but there is plenty that you can be getting on with. What you must not do is start to become committed to detailed plans, however strong the impulse is to do it. The reasons for this are dealt with in the section of this book covering 'Site Analysis'. However, what you can do is spend some enjoyable time putting together a design brief, ready to hand over to your chosen designer on the day that your offer on a plot is accepted. The object of the exercise is to provide a comprehensive description of your requirements, tempered, perhaps, by the realisation that you can't have everything (unless you are an Arab oil sheikh, or a lottery winner). But there is no harm in a spot of daydreaming to keep you going.

There are many decisions that should be made and recorded before design work begins in earnest. You may not want to have to think about some of them, and prefer to launch straight into briefing a designer to see what they come up with. This will not only waste the architect's time, it is also rather unfair to expect your dream home to be produced without a fairly thorough briefing process – any success would be down to chance rather than skill. For example, there is nothing more depressing for a designer to be told how a carefully thought-out scheme that cleverly uses the roof space looks horrible, or that the living room is too small. The obvious way to avoid this is to make clear your passionate hatred of dormer windows, and your ownership of a grand piano, *before* the design drawings are started. This principle holds good for all your important requirements, right down to the detailed construction.

One of the basic rules of preparing a brief is that you write down all information, and share it with the rest of the family who are involved. This can provoke some unexpected discussion or disagreements, but it is better to have these arguments early on, rather than in front of the architect who has just spent several days preparing an unwittingly controversial design.

What Information Ought to be Covered by a Design Brief?

The short answer to this question is: anything that you think is important. If the only thing that really matters to you is the number of rooms, or that there is space for your collection of historic military uniforms, that is all you have to put into it. Most people have a lot more to say than this of course, because the brief goes to the heart of the matter – achieving these things is the whole reason for embarking on the project in the first place. Some briefs have been known to run to several A4 ring-binders, but this is counter-productive. The whole point is to identify the things that are essential, and record them in a way that is intelligible to someone else. The following are some suggestions as to what you should consider for inclusion in your brief.

- budget summary and area calculation
- photos of buildings and features/details/materials that you like
- photos of buildings and features/details/materials that you *don't* like
- preferred construction method(s)
- how the building is likely to be built, and by whom
- magazine articles and extracts
- Lifestyle List - the requirements of each family member
- schedule of rooms required
- Room Information Sheets (see Table 9 in 'Preparing a Brief' section, below)

Each family member should try to list the aspects of the brief crucial to them, such as 'sustainability', or 'ease of maintenance', in order of importance, then compare lists. The difference is usually very educational.

Appearance

The style and appearance of your home are the most subjective things in the brief. The subject of style is highly emotive and may lead to the biggest disagreements within the family, but try to keep an open mind. One person's design feature is another's 'carbuncle'. There is a huge range of styles available, and some people find this intimidating, but everyone knows what they don't like – so this is one possible starting point. It is just as important to communicate this to whoever designs your house as letting them know what you do like.

The best way to record your inclinations is to find some illustrations – a picture really is worth a thousand words. Cut out and keep photos from magazines; keep a camera handy, and take your own pictures of houses that interest you. Take some time to go around the showhouses on the local new estates (with your camera) and ask for brochures, which indicate the designs and plans of the properties you visit. Talk to architects and designers, visit exhibitions and read as many magazines as you can get hold of. Your aim is to become visually literate enough to understand why some buildings are more attractive to you than others.

ASBA Four Square Design

Photo: Nigel Rigden/*Homebuilding & Renovating*

ASBA Mole Architects

ASBA Reed Architects

Collect as many pictures of buildings that interest you as you can.

Table 4: Preferred Features and Materials List
This form is designed to be copied, filled in and handed to your designer
External Structure *(e.g. brick, render and timber frame, stone, part tile-hung, shiplap timber boarding)*
Internal Structure *(e.g. masonry, timber frame, solid walls, solid floors)*
External Windows and Doors, Material and Style *(e.g. softwood, hardwood, upvc, casement, cottage-style)*
Internal Doors, Material and Style *(e.g. flush, 4-panelled, 6-panelled)*
Style *(eg. Victorian, Georgian, vernacular)*
Building Elements *(e.g. separate or detached garage, conservatory)*
Other Major Features *(e.g. energy efficiency, low maintenance, easy-to-build, room-in-the-roof, basement)*

Invest in a cheap camera, to keep permanently in the car and quickly snap pictures if you pass anything that may be a useful clue to how you would like your house to look. But beware of angry house owners, who may mistake you for a burglar 'casing the joint'!

The object of the exercise at this stage is to come up with a list of preferred construction-types and materials for your house. If you examine the information that you have collected, there are likely to be some consistent themes, e.g. particular styles and features that crop up more than others. Using these clues, you should be able to take a stab at completing the form listing your preferences.

Construction Method

There are plenty of alternatives to the most popular construction method of brick and block, and whichever method you choose will have a profound effect on your project. Ideally the decision should be made before design work starts, because it may place limitations on, or bring benefits to, the design that should be considered from the start (see Table 5: 'Comparison of Timber Frame and Brick and Block Construction', below).

The best way to differentiate between construction methods is to look at the structure of the building, not the external cladding. This is because, for example, timber and render can be planted on to the face of blockwork walls to make it look like the building has been made with a timber frame. Conversely, lighter construction methods can be finished by cladding them in brick, to imitate masonry construction. If the house is also dry-lined with plasterboard, rather than wet-plastered, the internal partitions will sound hollow when tapped,creating the illusion of timber stud walls.

Don't confuse the method of procurement – or how you get your house built – with the method of construction. Timber frame is readily available in 'bespoke' form and you don't necessarily need to choose a kit supplier's design to get one.

Prefabrication

Many of the alternatives to masonry construction have been developed to 'de-skill' some of the building work on site, by prefabricating large parts of the structure in a factory. They appeal to developers because, although initial costs are higher, they lead to a quicker construction time on site, with a reduced risk of errors or poor workmanship. The different systems available vary from a bundle of materials that arrive cut to size and needing to be assembled (but not fabricated) on site, to 'cassettes', which are whole rooms that are craned into position and stacked on top of each other.

The greater the extent of prefabrication, the more expensive a one-off design becomes, but the unit cost reduces if the same design is repeated many times. Prefabricated systems are good for self builders who are planning to do a lot of the work themselves, because the fast erection time on site means that they are free to get on with the less skilled work inside a secure, dry envelope. Some of the systems can even be assembled by a self builder, although these are quite expensive to buy, so there is less advantage if builders are being paid to work on site.

The use of prefabricated systems of all kinds is increasing and, due to the ever-declining number of skilled tradesmen in the UK, will almost certainly continue to do so.

Timber Frame or Brick and Block?

Masonry is the most common method of construction for one-off homes in the UK, but timber frame is growing in popularity. For a full comparison between masonry and the main types of timber frame used see Comparison Table 5, below.

Table 5: Comparison of Conventional Timber Frame and Brick and Block Construction

Contrary to what each camp will tell you, neither method is inherently superior to the other. But one method may suit your own project better than the other. This table compares their strengths and weaknesses, regardless of whether a pre-designed kit or a bespoke timber frame is used.

Aspect of Design	UK Standard Brick and Block	UK Standard Timber Frame
Thermal Insulation	Up to 100 mm can easily be accommodated in the cavity - if insulation is thicker than this special cavity ties are needed of the extra insulation must be fixed to the inside surface of the wall.	Typical stud walls are up to 140 mm wide. If more insulation is needed, it can be fixed to the inside surface of the wall.
Thermal Response	Heats up slowly, cools down slowly.	Building heats up quickly, cools down quickly.
Sustainability/Eco-friendliness	Blocks are made by recycling waste materials.	Timber can be regrown and is 'sustainable'.
DIY	Many DIY enthusiasts are familiar with the techniques needed.	Usually built by specialist suppliers; only experienced DIYers should attempt to build the frame themselves.
Familiarity	Most contractors are very familiar with the required building techniques.	Unless you are in Scotland, the average builder will not be very familiar with timber-frame construction. But, assuming it is built by the supplier, it reduces reliance on skilled trades such as bricklayers and plasterers.
On-site Improvisation	Easy to alter, or correct errors, on site; plenty of tolerance of inexact building.	If prefabricated, requires precision in preparing the groundworks, foundations and slab.
Up-front Costs	Builders and merchants are paid after delivery.	Will require a significant deposit on ordering.
Delivery Times	Readily available at builders' merchants, although particular bricks may have delivery times of 6–8 weeks.	Typically on site 12–16 weeks after ordering.
Post-Construction Alterations	Easily done by a competent builder.	If prefabricated, harder to alter on site and after construction.
Speed of Erection	Relatively slow to watertight stage. After a few courses have been laid, the mortar has to set before the next course can be built above them.	Very quick to watertight stage (e.g. 7 days).
Building in Poor Weather	Difficult: mortar and concrete are particularly vulnerable to defects if it is wet, or near freezing.	Much less vulnerable to short-term weather conditions, although, if it gets too damp, timber will shrink and move as it dries.
Retention of Moisture after Construction	Masonry will retain moisture, and release it slowly into the house for many months. This is harmless, but causes higher humidity levels than expected until it has dissipated.	A relatively 'dry' process, but, if excessive moisture gets trapped inside the walls, there is a serious risk of rot occurring.
Quality Control	Mainly on site, needs constant checking to avoid defects, particularly where they could be concealed in the cavity.	If prefabricated, quality is factory-controlled. Any defects are readily visible on site.
External Appearance	No real effect, can be clad with anything.	No real effect, can be clad in anything, including brick.
Ease of Fixing Shelves, etc. to the Inside Walls	Standard blockwork is easy to screw into. Very lightweight blocks require special fixings.	Heavy fixtures like shelving need to be fixed into studs, so they have to be pre-planned, or the studs have to be found behind the plasterboard after construction.
Sound Insulation Between Rooms	Relatively easy to achieve. Masonry internal walls and solid precast concrete upper floors easily give a good level of sound insulation.	Much harder to achieve, although similar levels to blockwork are possible. Block walls on upper floors are not possible, neither are precast concrete upper floors.
Sound Transmission From Outside	Very good. Masonry absorbs sound easily.	Less good – but can be clad in brickwork, which helps.

Start with your requirements for the project and then see which building method addresses them, rather than deciding on a particular design or system and then altering your project to fit in with it.

Masonry Construction

Older masonry walls are made from a single leaf of brick, as thick as the longest dimension of a brick (called a stretcher). Their modern equivalent has a cavity – usually containing insulation, and sometimes with an air gap as well – and uses cheaper, concrete blocks on the inside. The outer leaf is either brick or block. The latter is sometimes clad in timber or tiles, or rendered.

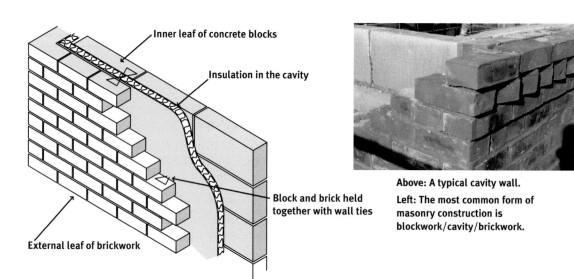

Inner leaf of concrete blocks

Insulation in the cavity

Block and brick held together with wall ties

External leaf of brickwork

Above: A typical cavity wall.

Left: The most common form of masonry construction is blockwork/cavity/brickwork.

Standard Timber Frame

The panels for a standard UK timber frame arrive on site as a combination of timber studs with a panel sheathing on one side. The panels are bolted together, the void between the studs is filled with insulation (usually 90 mm thick) and then covered with a barrier to stop moisture entering and condensing inside it, and lined with plasterboard. The outside of the sheathing has a 'breather membrane' placed across it, which allows damp air to evaporate to the outside, but stops water finding its way into the construction. The outside can be rendered, or clad in brickwork. The Scandinavian version of this type of construction goes one better, in that the whole wall is constructed in the factory and put together in a matter of hours on site with a crane. The latter is called a 'closed' frame system, and the UK version is called an 'open' frame system.

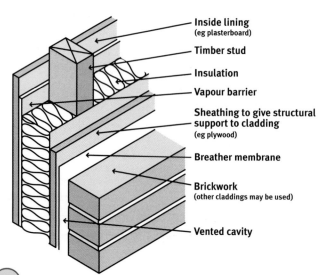

Inside lining
(eg plasterboard)

Timber stud

Insulation

Vapour barrier

Sheathing to give structural support to cladding
(eg plywood)

Breather membrane

Brickwork
(other claddings may be used)

Vented cavity

Above: A timber-framed house under construction.

Left: A typical example of the most commonly used type of timber frame in the UK.

An example of a house built from
a concrete building system.

This builder is sticking bricks together with glue,
rather than laying them in mortar.

Post-and-beam house.

Oak-framed house.

Careful choice of materials make this new house look
like it has been around for centuries.

Thin-Joint Block

Block manufacturers, aware of some of the limitations presented by blockwork, have devised a way of laying them that requires less skill, is faster, reduces retained moisture and drying times, and results in a smoother finish that does not need a thick coat of plaster to hide any irregularities. It involves gluing the blocks together with an adhesive, rather than bedding them in mortar. The walls are finished by spraying a fine coat of plaster and render on either side. As with many alternative building methods, the system has been used successfully in other countries – in this case, in Scandinavia. One company has extended the idea to achieve a complete building system, including precast concrete floors and roof panels. The end result in design terms is a building with very flat, clean walls, usually rendered, with open roof spaces, and quite rectilinear overall because this form suits the system better.

Post-and-Beam Timber Frame

Instead of using the panels as structural sheets to take the loads on the walls, posts and beams can be used to construct a frame, which is then clad with panels (which do not perform a structural role). The benefit to the design is that the gaps between the posts can be left completely free of structure, allowing large areas of glass. It also provides a flexible internal layout, which can be altered easily, provided that the posts do not have to be moved.

Oak Frame

Anyone who has admired the 'Tudor' style timber frames built in Britain since medieval times will appreciate the benefits of a house built with traditional materials, using tried-and-tested building methods such as these. It is highly skilled work and uses a relatively expensive building material, and this is reflected in the cost, which is around 30–50 per cent over the cost of a similar building using a modern system. However, the resulting designs look authentically old, and allow the use of timber as a construction material to be celebrated to its best advantage.

Structurally Insulated Panels (SIPs)

'SIPs' are currently a buzzword in the UK construction industry, and are quickly mentioned whenever prefabrication is being discussed. But unsurprisingly, our fellow Europeans have been happily using them for many decades. They are nothing more than sandwiches – a thick layer of highly insulating material (polyurethane, or something similar), factory-bonded to sheets of strong board. They are light and strong, and give a very high insulation value. They can be used structurally, or as cladding. You can buy a pre-designed house, with all the structure factory-made and delivered to site ready to be assembled, or cut the boards on site with a saw. The high insulation value of the walls means that you can agree to 'trade off' the heat loss from glazing with the building control officer, who will then permit larger areas of glass than the Building Regulations would allow for a less-well-insulated house.

A steel-framed house by Richard Murphy Architects.

This house is built from hollow polystyrene blocks filled with concrete.

Steel Frame

This is little-used in Britain for houses, and hardly used at all for one-offs, although the main reason is probably due to misplaced prejudice, owing to it not being a traditional building material, rather than any rational reason. A steel frame is used in a similar way to the panel-based timber framed systems, but greater spans are possible, allowing larger areas of glass and open-plan spaces.

Expanded Polystyrene filled with Mass Concrete (PIFs)

Sometimes referred to as Permanent Insulated Formwork, these products are hollow blocks of polystyrene, which slot together on site with steel reinforcing over openings to form lintels, and which are then filled with mass concrete. Formwork in the conventional sense is the timber shuttering used to hold concrete in place while it sets. Here, the polystyrene plays the same role, but stays in place and provides insulation at the same time. The process is 'self-build-friendly' because, after some basic training, the blocks are fairly easy to assemble – and because they are very lightweight there are fewer health and safety risks for amateurs on the building site. They are particularly effective for forming basements, being watertight, and above ground are usually rendered.

Rammed Earth, Cob and Earth Bricks

All these building methods use an abundant natural material, which is compacted one way or another, dried, and protected from the elements. Several houses a year are built this way by enthusiasts, and make perfectly serviceable homes. Only certain kinds of earth are suitable, and specialist advice – well beyond the scope of this book – is essential. The limitations imposed lead to some distinctive buildings. Most people will be familiar with the gently curving whitewashed walls typical of traditional houses in Devon, and the Southwest of England generally, all built with cob construction.

Straw Bales

Another method – much favoured by environmentalists, who like to see the effective use of natural material – straw can be used in bales to support its own weight up to a limited height, or as an infill material. It has excellent insulation properties, but needs to be carefully protected from the weather, impact and rodents.

Procurement Route

A crucial part of the brief for your project is consideration of the way that you will get it built, otherwise known as your 'procurement route'. You may think that you can leave a decision on this until later. This would, however, be misplaced optimism, because how you build your house will affect the budget, the time-scale and most importantly your peace of mind.

There are several basic procurement routes, all with subtle variations, and which one is right for you will depend on many factors, such as your budget, personal skills and time-availability. All kinds of people from all kinds of backgrounds have successfully completed a project with any one of these methods, but some overconfident families have got into difficulties by wrongly assuming that they will have the resources and abilities to play a major role on site.

DIY Self Build

Taking on most of the building work yourself is an option that should only be considered by the most determined and enthusiastic self builders. It is rare for anyone to actually complete every task personally – not least because certain tasks, such as fitting a boiler, are definitely for the qualified. The main attraction of building this way – apart from the challenge – is the reduced cost, achieved by cutting out the profit taken by the main contractor and the expense of hiring labour. The benefits of this approach have increased in recent times, due to the lack of skilled building workers and the consequent increase in their wages. However, these savings can be offset by the builders' merchants

Even the most determined DIY enthusiast needs help sometimes.

and suppliers charging higher prices. They are reluctant to offer self builders the same level of discount available to long-term customers. To circumvent this, some builders' merchants offer group discount schemes that self builders can join, which can help to lower prices.

Apart from the reduced costs, the other common feature of DIY is the extra time required to complete the project. The build programme can be two or three times longer than an experienced contractor would take. The pressure to complete means that most leisure time is taken up working on the house. Progress is slowed, as new skills have to be learnt and old ones brushed up. Apart from the building work, the DIY self builder has to deal with the management side as well. Site safety, insurance, ordering of materials and dealing with building control officers all need to be accounted for. Sometimes, to avoid these kinds of difficulties, a hybrid of the full DIY route is used, where the 'shell' is constructed by a contractor, leaving a watertight structural box, and the self builders then sort out the electrical installation, plumbing, plastering and decorating themselves.

If you have already built your own extension or renovated a property, don't make the mistake of assuming that a house will be a similar experience, only bigger. Building a house is far more complex in construction and organisational terms.

Although you should have a carefully monitored cost plan and you must comply with planning requirements and Building Regulations, you are free to make design decisions and change the specification as work progresses. Any design decisions taken from an early stage must allow for ease of construction, and products or construction methods that require a high level of building skill not possessed by the DIY enthusiast are best avoided. For example, the plan should be kept as simple and rectilinear as possible, roof shapes should be kept straightforward (possibly avoiding hips in favour of gables) and you may chose interlocking tiles rather than slates or plain tiles, which are harder to fix.

The shape of this house was kept very simple, to make it easier to build and to keep down costs.

Self Manage

Rather than carry out all the work, you can hire individual trades – either on a fixed price or daily rate – to do most of it for you. You then will take on the role that is usually played by the main contractor – that is, buying some of the materials, finding and employing individuals and subcontractors, performing the site management role, and possibly carrying out some of the less critical work (e.g. decorating). Money is saved, because you do not have to pay some of a contractor's overheads, and you keep all of the profit that they would look for. The total of both these items typically amounts to 10–20 per cent on the building cost. Although overheads such as office costs are saved, the usual site management costs, like insurances, still have to be paid. The absence of builders' merchants' discounts, etc. will reduce savings in the same way as for someone who takes the DIY route.

It is a mistake, however, to think that building contractors get their percentage easily. It is usually hard won by astute bargaining, shrewd business acumen and the skillful management of people. A self manager will have to go some way towards matching these skills in order to make the exercise worthwhile. As well as management skills, you also need the time to apply them – not just a certain number of hours in the week; you sometimes have to be available at specific times of the day as well. If a problem develops on site, it may need to be sorted out straight away, and deliveries of supplies may require you to be there to check and sign for them. For this reason, many self managers tend to be people whose job allows them flexible working hours – such as the self employed, or senior management. A common problem for self managers is that subcontractors and trades fail to turn up on the appointed day, or leave a job part way through. This is because they can afford to offend (and lose) a one-off client, and will do so rather than let down a contractor who employs them regularly.

Apart from assuming the role of the contractor, you will also assume the risk taken. A contractor who quotes a fixed price for an accurately specified job gambles on their ability to accurately price and properly manage the project. If they do well, they make more profit. If they do badly, they will lose money – the price to the client is the same. If you are managing the project and you get it wrong, you will lose money – or, in the worst case, run out of finance and have to abandon the whole project.

Conversely, as many self builders have found, the rewards are high if you are able to succeed, allowing you to jump several rungs up the housing ladder.

To take this route successfully you must have the design and specification worked out well before each stage or trade is started, so that payment can be agreed and the work programmed in. However, you may be able to incorporate products and materials that you come across as the project proceeds on site, since you can make design changes later in the programme than if you were using a single contractor. You can also more easily trim or expand the amount you spend on fittings and finishes, towards the end of the building work. But in general, the fewer areas of work which rely on specialist contractors, the better, since these will be the hardest and most expensive for you to employ.

In the case of a complex design with several different materials, call in the experts.

In particular, complex designs that involve the use of unusual materials, and require the co-ordination of several different suppliers and contractors, increase the risk of problems for you if they do not perform. For example, a complex roof design, using bespoke manufactured elements and materials unusual to domestic construction – such as a standing-seam metal roof supported on specially designed composite timber beams – may require the co-ordination of three or four manufacturers and a corresponding number of trades on site.

Project Management

If you are sufficiently aware to realise that you do not have the skills to self manage, the next best thing is to find someone to manage on your behalf – in other words, to find a project manager.

 If you are about to start asking around for a project manager, make sure that whoever you speak to understands what you mean by this.

In the commercial construction industry, a project manager is someone who represents the client through the whole design and construction process, usually on very large projects. The word is used in the domestic market to mean something quite different – someone who generally acts as the client's representative on site. This rather loose description invites a lot of confusion; before discussing fees with such a person, you must explicitly define what you need them to do.

Some of the things that a project manager may – or may not – do for you

- very approximate budget costings (that they cannot be held responsible for if they are wrong)
- accurate budget costings
- lists of quantities of materials (materials schedules)
- project programming
- cost monitoring as work progresses
- locating and negotiating with trades and subcontractors
- quality control on site (snagging)
- management of personnel on site, including discipline and hiring and firing
- progress and payment certificates acceptable to building societies and any future purchaser's solicitor
- ensuring that the Building Regulations are complied with, and that the work is constructed in accordance with the drawings and specifications
- approving work and authorising payment
- ensuring that the required insurances are in place
- ensuring that health and safety legislation is complied with

One thing to note in the list of possible services is the use of the word 'ensuring'. Simply providing a list of the health and safety requirements, or even handing it out to anyone who visits the site, is not the same as 'ensuring' that they are complied with. Someone has to take responsibility for these things, and if the project manager doesn't, it will be you. Ignorance is no defence if someone gets hurt, and a criminal charge of failing to comply with the regulations could be in the offing – not to mention damages due to the injured party. The more work, and the more liability, that a project manager takes on, the higher their fee. Consequently, a full service covering everything is likely to make the final project-cost similar to that incurred by using a single main contractor.

Once you have an idea of what you need doing, you have to find a project manager, which is usually not an easy task. There are not sufficient self builds around to generate many specialist project managers who are fully conversant with self builds and their specific requirements (except in areas like Milton Keynes, where self builds have been encouraged by the government). Most of the people with the relevant skills find more profit in working for a contractor or developer. There are organisations who will put you in touch with a project manager, or at least someone who may offer a partial project-management service. Alternatively, small local builders, who do not necessarily want a relatively large project to go through their books, may perform a site-based management service if you make it worth their while. However, they may wish to have some direct involvement in the purchase of materials and the hiring of some subcontractors, and may charge it by taking a percentage fee on top of their management fee. The latter may be either a percentage (their risk) or a weekly rate (your risk). Do not employ architects, quantity surveyors or building surveyors for this kind of work unless they can prove that they have a track record in this field – actual site management is beyond the typical skill-set of these professionals.

If you are lucky enough to employ a skilled project manager, you should have as much design freedom as if you were using a main contractor – but remember that you will still carry most of the risk if things go wrong.

Main Contractor

The lowest risk, but potentially higher-cost, route is the one most familiar both to clients and the building industry. Here, the client arranges for a full set of working drawings to be prepared and the contractor submits a fixed price quotation (as opposed to the more approximate 'estimate'). The contractor then builds for the quoted price, for completion at an agreed date. The contractor can only ask for more payment if there are design changes, and may have to pay you compensation if the project overruns. Very often, an independent professional is employed to manage the contract on the client's behalf (see section on Appointing an Architect in 'Finding a Designer', later). As a result, you have a pretty reliable idea of what the cost of the finished house will be, which makes financial planning much easier.

The idea with this procurement route is that the contractor takes most of the risk, and to make sure that this happens it is vital to ensure that a full set of working drawings are prepared, along with a detailed specification, before any prices are quoted. Frequently, contractor-run projects go over budget and time when this advice is ignored. Getting this work done means that there is an unavoidable up-front cost that must be paid, but this will save far more money in the long run, by avoiding extras or changes on site.

If you want to use unusual products or an unconventional construction method, make sure that you or your designers talk to the suppliers and manufacturers. They have a vested interest in your project going well, and often will carry out design and specification work, or even provide training for the builders on site, at no extra cost.

As far as the design goes, everything should really be decided before work starts on site, if possible. There is then more scope for innovation and bespoke construction, and contractors can be selected who have the right experience of any unusual or special aspects of the design.

Design-Build

This is the lowest-risk/highest-cost route to procuring your house. A single contractor is approached after planning-approval stage, or sometimes before the design is completed. A price is agreed for an outline specification, and the builder then manipulates the design, specification and construction to hit this target. The theory is that the price is known and agreed at an early stage. But even the most experienced contractor cannot know how much a bespoke building will cost until the detailed information has been prepared and priced, so the price will be high to cover the extra risk. With design and build, the competitive element is lost and there is no reliable way of comparing prices between contractors. Many contractors find it hard to resist the temptation to either reduce the specification, in ways that are not immediately obvious on site, or to increase the price whenever the client changes the agreed design.

The loss of control of the design and specification of the project means that this route is often not favoured by anyone who wants an individual, one-off house. Many contractors find it a difficult way of working as well, because they find that a lot of their decisions (and therefore their costings) are changed as the project progresses, and possibly even once work has begun on site. It works best if standard house types are used, with detailed specifications available at an early stage.

Table 6: Which Procurement Method is Best For You?					
Procurement Method	**DIY**	**Self-Managed**	**Project Manager**	**Main Contractor**	**Design-Build**
Risk Level	Very High	High	Medium	Lower	Lowest
Time Demand	Very High	Very High	Medium	Low	Lowest
Time Needed	As much as possible – at least several days per week, some in working hours (i.e. Monday – Friday).	At least one or two days, during working hours, per week.	A few early mornings/evenings, during working hours, per week; plus one or two days at the weekend per month.	Several half-days, during working hours, and a few other days per month.	One or two half-days, during working hours, per month.
Practical Skills	Essential	Essential	Helpful	Not Essential	Not Essential
Organisational Skills	Essential	Essential	Helpful	Not Essential	Not Essential
Cost Awareness	Essential, in detail	Essential, in detail	Important	Important, but in overview	Not Important
Typical Contingency at Start on Site	Very High – at least 10–15%	Very High – at least 10–15%	High – at least 10%	5–10%	5%
Cash Flow	Hard to plan and predict accurately.	Hard to plan and predict accurately.	Should have a reasonably accurate budget plan.	Payment at agreed intervals (e.g. monthly), approximate amounts known at start.	At agreed intervals (e.g. monthly), amounts known accurately at start.

Lifestyle

A major part of your brief should centre on how you expect to use the new house as a place to live. Your home should be tailored to the individual needs and aspirations of your family, and be able to adapt and grow around its occupants. To ensure that your design will do this, you need to find out exactly what those needs and aspirations are, and make sure your designer knows about them in advance.

A good place to start you quest for 'self-enlightenment' is your current home. A critical eye cast around is one thing – most people know what they would like to change about their present house. But there is far more that you can learn from looking at your current lifestyle, if you begin to examine it in detail. Some the points covered in this section can be evolved by thinking about what you do now, how you do it, and how it can be changed and improved. A simple early trick is to measure the building plot and the house plan of your current home, and work our approximate areas of the rooms. Occasionally, self builders are surprised to learn that they don't necessarily need a bigger house, just one with the spaces arranged in a different way.

The following list covers some of the most important areas to consider. A few may be irrelevant to you, but this is just as important for the architect to know as the things that are dear to your heart.

Daily Routine

When is the house to be used, and by whom? You may be surprised at what happens in your home when you are not there. When you do something and where you do it, and the sequence of events, should influence the plan of the new home.

Table 7, below, illustrates a typical day in the life of a family house. That is not to suggest that you need to prepare a detailed 'time-and-motion study' like this, but it still needs to be thought about. For example, this family clearly needs a place, or places, where the TV can be watched without

Table 7: A Typical Weekday Schedule for Family				
Time of Day	Mum	Dad	15-Year-Old Daughter	9-Year-Old Son
Very Early Morning	Asleep	Sometimes up for work	Asleep	Asleep
Early Morning	Breakfast, etc.	Usually getting ready for work	Asleep until just before school	Breakfast, etc.
Mid Morning	Out at work/ occasionally sleeping	Sometimes works from home	Out at school	Out at school
Late Morning	Out at work/ occasionally sleeping	Sometimes works from home	Out at school	Out at school
Lunchtime	Eating lunch	Out at work	Out at school	Out at school
Early Afternoon	Housework	Out at work	Out at school	Out at school
Mid Afternoon	Collecting son from school	Out at work	Out at school	Out at school
Late Afternoon	Friends round for coffee	Out/sometimes works from home	Out	Doing homework
Early Evening	Having tea & watching TV	Out/sometimes works from home	Out	Having tea & Watching TV
Mid Evening	Housework	Having tea	Having tea	Watching TV
Late Evening	Usually sleeping	Watching TV	Doing homework/ out with friends/ listening to music	Asleep
Overnight	Occasional shift work	Asleep	Asleep	Asleep

disturbing some of the other family members who are asleep or doing homework. Also they need to be able to eat comfortably as they watch TV. People must be able to come and go in the night or early morning, without disturbing those who are asleep. There may be a need for a room to be used as a study/office, away from the rest of the house. These requirements should influence the design of the house and also its construction – there is a strong case for solid walls, for instance, to insulate against sound for this family.

The whole family should be considered, including existing and potential pets. For example, dogs need somewhere to sleep, a secure garden and somewhere to run off mud before entering the house – such as entrance through a utility room (cats, of course, don't bother with these things – they just expect to be treated like a particularly favoured child).

Rooms, Their Uses and Connections

At this stage it is more important to think about the spaces that you need, rather than necessarily how those spaces will be partitioned off as rooms, an aspect that can be developed as part of the design. There are two levels on which to think about rooms: how they relate to each other, and how they relate to the activities that go on inside them.

Draw up a list of the rooms that you would ideally like to have, and decide which are essential, which you would quite like and which are really a luxury. Bear in mind that most in the last category are likely to be crossed off the list as the design work starts and the budget begins to bite, but you may at least be able incorporate one or two of them. Think about each room, and question whether you actually need it. This is your house, and you don't have to have a dining room just because the

Table 8: List of Rooms or Spaces Required							
Room or Space	Combined With (other room name)	Essential (tick)	Desirable (tick)	Luxury (tick)	Length	Width	Area
Ground Floor							
Kitchen							
Utility Room (downstairs)							
Dining Room							
Living Room							
TV Room							
Study							
Family Room							
Conservatory							
Workshop							
WC (Required by Building Regulations)							
Cloaks							
Hall and Corridor (e.g. 10% of floor area)							
First Floor							
Bedroom 1							
En suite to Bedroom 1							
Dressing Room to Bedroom 1							
Bedroom 2							
En suite to Bedroom 2							
Dressing Room to Bedroom 2							
Bedroom 3							
En suite to Bedroom 3							
Bedroom 4							
En suite to Bedroom 4							
Bedroom 5							
En suite to Bedroom 5							
Bathroom							
Utility Room (upstairs)							
Study							
Landing & Corridor (e.g. 10% of floor area)							
Second Floor							
Bedroom							
En suite							
Bedroom							
En suite							
Bathroom							
Landing & Corridor (e.g. 10% of floor area)							

Don't forget to allow for wall thicknesses and circulation area when you calculate your desirable house size.

average house in an estate has one, especially if you don't think it will be used except at Christmas time. If you're thinking in terms of areas that must be earmarked for a use, rather than actual rooms, you may find that some of them can be combined. For example, many families prepare food, eat it and socialise in one space, which used to be called the kitchen, but is nowadays better described as the kitchen/dining area/family room. You may prefer to have a large living room, which has one end devoted to reading and chatting and the other for watching TV, rather than two separate rooms.

In order to fill in the whole form shown here, you will have to have a stab at guessing what size the rooms need to be, and that will require a bit more work – illustrated by Table 9, which is headed 'Room Information Sheet'.

Room Information Sheet

To use this sheet, copy it and fill it in for each room that is important to you. At the very start of preparing your brief, you will not be able to provide much of the information on these sheets, but they are designed to be updated as the project progresses, and to act as a useful prompt as to the sort of information that is going to be needed. If you don't make these decisions, then someone else will do it for you, which may be fine in some cases, but mostly it is better for you to have thought through what does and doesn't matter to you. All the items listed will have a direct effect on the design, and in some cases the construction as well. There will certainly be implications for the budget, too.

Whose Room is It?

Who is to use a room is usually obvious, but not necessarily – asking this question may spark a discussion about whether the kids can use the living room or whether it should be kept for 'best', whilst they build their Lego or lounge around listening to music in the family room. Who uses the room most might perhaps, in the event of a disagreement, be allowed to decide how it is designed, equipped and finished off.

The connections between rooms will be useful in developing the early sketch plans, and it is surprising how these can differ between families, depending on their lifestyle. For example, some people like to have the living room, kitchen and

One space can serve many purposes.

Photo: Nigel Rigden/*Homebuilding & Renovating*

conservatory all linked, with double doors between, so that they can be opened out into one large space. Whereas others like the kitchen to be well out of site, and would be mortified if guests could see the state it gets into.

Table 9: Room Information Sheet
Room Name:
Room Uses and Activities. Main Uses: Other Uses:
People Who Will Use the Room.
Connected to Which Other Spaces?
Position (e.g. 'at the back', facing the morning sun, etc.)
Fitted Furniture and Fixtures (eg. shelves, cupboards, TV cabinet, bath, WC pan, washing machine, etc.)
Loose Furniture (e.g. dining table, piano, desk, bed, etc.) State sizes if possible.
Loose Electrical Appliances (e.g. TV, computer, desk lamp, radio, etc.)
Communications (e.g. cable TV, telephone socket, co-axial cable for TV, CAT 5, etc.)
Lighting (e.g. pendant, wall-washers, spots, mini-spots, track, mirror light).
Other Critical Space Requirements (e.g. to do aerobics, to do the ironing, etc.)
Finishes (e.g. paint, wallpaper, stain, etc.) Wall: Floor: Ceiling: Woodwork:
Other Requirements (e.g. inglenook fireplace, etc.)
Approximate Dimensions. Preferred: Minimum:

Connected to Which Other Spaces?

Deciding how rooms join up to each other is the first basic step in designing a house plan. At this stage, it is not necessary to launch into experimenting with room layouts in detail, but it is possible to draw out some 'bubble diagrams', which you can use to develop you ideas as to how the rooms should link up. These deceptively simple drawings require no particular skill, but can help you make some basic decisions together with your family, and can be very informative to your designer.

A simple bubble diagram can be used to generate the best layout for the house.

Furniture

Some rooms may need to be at the back of the house, to enjoy the view of the garden and have some privacy, or to enable a parent to keep an eye on young children in the garden. Others, such as the kitchen, may need to be facing the front, to allow a good view of the world passing by and any visitors as they approach. At the beginning, you may not be all that sure what fitted or loose furniture you want in the rooms, but it is worth making some educated guesses because they will have an enormous influence on the size and shape that the room will have to be to accommodate them. How many people will sit around the dining table at Christmas? Where will that treasured heirloom, Aunt Mildred's Welsh Dresser, go (even if the answer is 'on the rubbish tip')?

Electrics and Lighting

A regular complaint about many new houses is that they do not have enough electrical sockets in the right locations. A brief glance through any home at the numerous TVs, DVDs, stereos, computers, Playstations etc. will soon explain how this happens. A little thought at an early stage will help ensure that your home has power supplies and phone sockets all in the right rooms, and that, if you have so many sockets that you need an extra ring mains, this is allowed for in the budget.

Another area neglected in many homes is the ability of lighting design to contribute to the quality of rooms and spaces in the house. More advanced home designers will think about what kind of activities take place in each room, and will allow for different kinds of lighting accordingly. Current technology allows you to pre-programme light settings according to what is going on in the room, e.g. bright task lighting for reading, background lights and wall-mounted uplighters for entertaining guests.

After any other special features for each room have been agreed, there should be enough information for you, or your architect, to make an educated guess as to the size that the room should be. It may even be worth experimenting with some graph paper and trying some notional room layouts, to see what kind of size and shape works best.

Once you have listed the rooms and estimated their sizes, you can add a bit for circulation, and reach a total area for your ideal house. This, in turn, can be compared with the area of house you can afford, which has been worked out as part of your budget calculations. At this point, virtually everyone who does this exercise then has to go back and decide which rooms either have to be reduced in size, or lost altogether. This process of review and re-evaluation is essential, and should carry on throughout the project – and needs to be carried out fairly ruthlessly to be effective.

Features and Materials

At this stage, you should also be able to have a fair stab at completing a list of the building materials and components that you want to be integrated into your new home. Your initial thoughts may be modified in the light of the location that you end up with, particularly if the local authority take an interest in what you are doing. You may wish your house to be in keeping with the area, but unless you are near a listed building or in a Conservation Area, you will still have plenty of choices available.

There is a huge range of materials available to be incorporated into a house, and many, such as bricks or roof tiles, need to be seen on an existing house to appreciate their full effect. Anyone who wishes to do the job of choosing them justice needs plenty of time to visit exhibitions, collect magazine articles, talk to sales reps and visit examples.

Sustainability and Energy Efficiency

An issue that is important to many is how 'green' or 'eco-friendly' the construction and design of their house should be. If this is a high priority for you, it is vital to identify the fact as early as possible. Current Building Regulations and planning practice already acknowledge the need to make modern homes far more respectful of the environment and natural resources than their predecessors. However, there are many ways in which you can improve on these minimum requirements – it is a question of how far you want to go, and how much you can afford. Sadly, many of the more radical options are expensive, and do not work out as economic for the average homebuilder, but, by careful design, it is possible to incorporate some of them at no extra cost. For example, putting a high proportion of the windows on the side of the house that faces south will increase heat-gain from the sun, and reduce the amount of energy needed to heat the house in winter.

You may need to do some investigation before you decide how far you want to go down the 'green' route, and you may face some interesting dilemmas. If you had to chose between an extra bedroom or a solar-powered heating system, which would you go for?

If you are going to look at this in hard financial terms, you should calculate the 'payback' time. This is where an aspect of the construction that initially costs more than expected, saves you money over time. For example, if extra insulation saves you a certain amount on your heating bill, how much do you save a year, and how long do you have to wait until you have recouped the money spent? At the moment, people buying houses do not seem to value energy-efficiency measures, in that they are reluctant to pay extra for them. So, although energy-efficient design is something to be encouraged, if you decide that you want an unusually high level of efficiency, then you should be aware that there is a cost, and have allowed for it in your budget.

In fact, self-build houses are generally more environment friendly than those built by developers, because the former are far more prepared to consider innovation and do put a value on these kinds of features in a house.

How long will you live there?

Another crucial question that you must ask yourself is how long you expect to live in the property. Your answer should fundamentally affect almost every decision that you take with respect to the design and specification of the building. If you expect to live in the house for many years, even decades, then, provided that you can afford it, you should make sure that you get as close as possible to your ideal. In this case, the resale value of the property may not be of any concern to you at all, provided that you can pay the mortgage. If you spend a little extra on a nice kitchen, or solid wood doors rather than laminated, you will get to enjoy them every day of your life for a long time to come.

However, if you plan to move after a few years, or want to sell the house fairly soon after occupying it, as a way of making extra income, a totally different approach is needed. A high-quality kitchen and better doors will not necessarily add any value to the sale price of the property. You have to think like a professional developer, and act like someone who puts profit in front of personal taste. Anyone reading this who is thinking 'of course we can', should think very carefully about this challenge. The truth is that many people who set out with this objective get sidetracked and seduced into following their own preferences and aspirations. To get it right, you should make it absolutely clear to your designers that this is what you intend to do and listen to their advice about the consequent planning and specification of the work.

Summary

At the end of this stage, you should have quite a reasonable idea of what you expect from your house – although, if you play by the rules, not a definitive house design. If you are methodical in gathering the information that makes up your brief, you should have a file that you can hand over to your architects at the first meeting after you have appointed them.

The development of a comprehensive brief is one of the most important steps in the design process, and is crucial to the success of the whole project. Many problems in the design and construction of buildings can be traced back to an inaccurate or inadequate brief. This applies just as much to large, public and commercial buildings as it does to your own project. On the other hand, a well-prepared brief gets the design off to a flying start, and allows you to keep everyone focused on the key reason for doing it in the first place – building yourself a home that makes the best use of the resources available to get you a design that is tailored to your family.

Finding a Site

Most people who want to build their own home find that the hardest part of the whole business is finding a site. You can get professionals to do virtually everything else for you if you so choose, but obtaining the land is mainly down to you. Occasionally people get lucky, but most families find their plots by a lengthy process that mixes a lot of determination with a little bit of luck. In the overcrowded, 'Nimby' UK, you are up against some fierce competition – other self builders, certainly, but also full-time 'land finders', small builders, and all the vested interests of the professional development industry.

It almost goes without saying that there is no point in starting to look for a site before you have worked out a budget. You should by now have identified the approximate size and quality of house that you are going to build, and have an idea of what you can afford for the land.

 Many of the techniques listed in this section are used by the professionals, but you have one significant advantage – you aren't one of them. Most vendors would far rather deal with a well-meaning amateur developer than a hard-nosed businessman whose only motivation is money.

None of these suggestions are a guaranteed route to a site, although some are easier to follow than others. For the best chance of success, try as many of them as you can manage.

Keep an Open Mind

The main reason that people fail to purchase a plot, is not necessarily that they fail to find any potential sites. It is because they will not compromise, and will accept nothing less than their dream plot, which in many cases simply does not exist. Before you start looking, think carefully about what you really need and what you would like, but also what you could do without. If you cannot compromise on anything, then be prepared for a long wait.

If you have some very rigid requirements about where you want to live, the constraints imposed by the kind of sites that are available may dictate what type of house you will build. On the other hand, if you have a firm idea of the character of the house you want to build, then you should be more flexible regarding the location. For example, if you want to live in a classic English village, the chances of getting planning approval for an innovative, modern design are, sadly, slim. If you can compromise and accept that to get this kind of property you will also have to consider a more urban environment, where the planners (and neighbours) may be more conducive to that kind of design, you improve your chances of achieving your main goal by widening the choice of plots.

Sometimes even the people selling a property may not realise that they have a potential building plot on their hands. If an existing property is in a very poor state, or structurally damaged, it may not be out of the question to demolish it and replace it with a new house. If you find a relatively small house on a large plot, this might also qualify for the same treatment. Sometimes a plot with a solitary bungalow on it can be replaced by several two-storey houses.

Desk Search

At the start of your search, you need to familiarise yourself with the area, and gather as much information on it as possible. Even if you're looking in your own neighbourhood, you may be surprised by what you find out with a little research. To be effective, you need to focus in on selected towns, villages or suburbs. If you pick too large an area at the start, your resources will be spread too thinly.

Maps

Ordnance Survey (OS) maps are full of useful information, and can help you to identify the areas that best suit your search criteria. The OS Pathfinder series (1:25,000 maps) are especially useful because they show streets and actual buildings, which are just about visible, and give a good indication of the density of development in an area. Look for areas that seem to have a fairly low density relative to other places on the map, i.e. where buildings are spaced further apart. These maps are also useful to refer back to when you identify a potential plot through other means. To complement these maps, there are aerial photographs of every county available for home computers, which are fun to use but, being fairly low-resolution pictures, are no use on their own.

Individual properties can just about be seen on the OS Pathfinder maps.

Local Plan

Local authority planning departments, in association with national government and county councils, prepare maps and plans of their area that identify which locations are suitable for new development, and the rules that will be used to govern infill sites. This information is published in the form of the Local Plan. It is a useful document, giving the background to planning policy, and can be browsed at the reception of the planning department.

At any given time, a revision of the Local Plan is usually in progress and if it is going to replace the existing one fairly soon it can give useful information on sites that may be released for development in the future. There is more information on how Local Plans work and the changes recently proposed by the Government in the 'Site Analysis' section of this book.

Planning Departments/Planning Register

Have you ever wondered why builders seem to hear about land, and purchase it, before it gets on the market? One reason is that they subscribe to data-collection companies that gather information on current planning applications and send out pre-selected lists of good leads. This also explains why, later on, when you make a planning application, you will get letters from builders marketing their services.

Your local town hall is a good source of information on potential building plots.

If anyone wishes to get planning approval to build on a piece of land, they must submit an application, which then becomes a matter of public record. What this means is that you can walk into any planning department and ask to see the Planning Register, in which all the applications and decisions (where they have been reached) are recorded. Many councils now publish them on their websites, but the ways in which they can be searched are rather limited – there is no substitute for being able to flip through a file. What you are looking for is recent applications, preferably outline (i.e. no detailed drawings), for single houses. If an approval has not come through, so much the better. A plot will not usually be advertised for sale until the planning approval has been granted, because this enhances the value, and, if someone spots it early enough, they can make an approach before many others are even aware that it is going to be for sale.

If you find a likely application, make a note of the applicant's details and approach them directly; they are usually, though not always, the owners of the plot. If the application is for outline approval there is a good chance that they are planning to sell, because there is no point in getting a detailed set of plans drawn up which may be changed by a purchaser. But sometimes they may have obtained detailed approval, with a full design, probably because the planners have insisted on it. Either way, there is no reason why you should not make a polite approach, either by letter or telephone.

Land Listing Agencies

There is not yet a service that collects planning data in a format suitable for people who are hunting for a single plot to build their own home, but there are some specialist agencies that collect information from estate agents and send lists of land out to subscribers, using the post and the Internet. These can save you a lot of legwork, and offer convenience. However, many people are getting the same information, and there is a time delay between the plot becoming available and you receiving the information. They are a useful starting point, and at the very least will help you to identify those agents who are active in selling land in your target areas. They will also give you an idea of how much land is coming on to the market, and at what sort of price.

Magazines

There are several magazines that are targeted at people who wish renovate a house or build their own home, and they all feature lists of land at the back. They are useful in the same way as the land-listing agencies, but the delay due to getting the magazine published, distributed and sold means that many of the best plots will have gone by the time you read about them. It is essential to take out a subscription if you intend to use them to help with your search, to ensure that you get your copy as soon as possible.

Local Papers

Most local papers have a section in the small ads listing 'Land for Sale' and usually there is a particular day that has more adverts than the rest of the week. Some have a weekly property supplement as well, which features adverts from estate agents and related features. If you do not live in the area you are searching, you can arrange to have the local paper posted to you, for whichever days you specify. They will arrive a few days late, but if a plot is going to be advertised, it will almost certainly be here.

English Partnerships

This government quango is responsible for New Towns, which are artificially created settlements, often on green-belt land. Their planning is more creative than most, and in the past they have supported all kinds of innovations, including making allowances for private one-off houses. Land is split into individual plots, and checks are made to ensure that they are not sold to developers or builders. There are also extra planning controls, to avoid an unpalatable mix of different styles occurring next to each other on the same road and to ensure that construction is completed in a reasonable time. Milton Keynes is a good example of this policy in action, but there are fewer plots available at the moment, and lots of competition to buy them.

Websites

There are many websites devoted to the marketing and sale of property. Some of them will give you more than just information on houses for sale, and will tell you about the areas you are looking at in some detail.

Networking

As with many other areas of life, who you know is as important as what you know. Out there are all kinds of people who will want to help you, once they know that you are looking. Some of them may even like the idea so much that they will agree to join you, to find more than one site. If this happens, you chances of success will immediately improve, because it will put double plots (or larger) within your budget, and will eliminate many other families from the competition – and you can choose your neighbours in advance.

Friends and Family

Most people already have a valuable source of help for finding a site, just waiting to be used: their relatives and acquaintances. Make sure that everyone that you know, in your family, business and social life knows that you are looking for some land. You may risk becoming a bore, but you may also set them thinking. A classic kind of plot for a one off-house is found in the garden of an existing property, so check out as many gardens as you can for this potential.

Some real examples of how 'Having Friends and Influencing People' can get you a site:

- The doctor who bought a garden belonging to a frail elderly patient who wanted her medical advisor close to hand.
- The family who looked for a plot for years, then demolished the bungalow they were living in and built a large house.
- Three work colleagues who were looking separately, found out about each other and ended up buying a triple plot together.
- A couple who built their house along the long driveway to their parents' house.
- The man who bought a piece of land that required permission from three impossibly awkward,

elderly sets of neighbours in order to be developed; made possible because he had lived next door as a child, and they trusted him alone.

- The man who would only sell part of his garden, a prime plot for a house, to his best friend from school.
- The couple who got planning policy changed so they could build in their garden, thanks to a petition signed by everyone in their village.
- An architect who gave up on his search for the day, went to the local pub for a rest, and was promptly told about an ideal plot.
- The estate agent who was approached to sell a plot and ended up building his own house on the site (one in every town).

Self-Build Collectives

There was a time when larger groups of people got together, formed their own company, and built their own houses together. This is rare now – perhaps because people are more individualistic, but also because the bureaucracy and legal obstacles are greater. However, such schemes do sometimes happen, usually driven by a committed individual, housing association or local authority. They tend to be low-cost schemes, partly grant funded, using 'sweat equity', i.e. people contributing their skills and labour in return for a share of the finished property. The Community Self Build Agency is an umbrella organisation that provides help and information to people who wish to build in this way.

Self-Build Clubs and Chatrooms

There is a club for self builders, the Association of Self Builders, and many Internet chatrooms, which are populated by other enthusiasts, some with experience, some in the same position as you. They can be a good source of advice throughout your project, and other self builders tend to be a helpful bunch of people, eager to share their experiences and help you avoid mistakes.

The Professionals

Estate Agents/Auctions

Despite being the most obvious professionals to go to when looking for land, not all estate agents will be able to help you. The commission to be earned on land is not as attractive as that for houses, and many agents – especially the large chains – have no interest in selling land. Local agents, or those which run auctions, are the most likely to have something of interest on their list, and there are usually at least one or two in a given area who will be willing to help.

Unfortunately, a few less-scrupulous agents would rather sell the land to someone with whom they have an ongoing relationship, like a local builder, because, apart from oiling the wheels of their business network, they are also likely to be the agent who gets the commission on the sale of the newly built house. So don't just leave your details with them and expect them to call you as soon as they hear of some land that may be of interest. Phone them regularly, and, if possible, visit them as well. If you are going to sell your house and then rent while you search for a plot, try to chose one of those agents who do sell land. The aim is to try to get into that magic drawer in every agent's office: the one with the list of 'hot' clients, who will get first crack at any good properties the agent is offered.

Architects

Architects come in all sorts of different guises, but there are some who have an interest in one off-houses and will know of land that is suitable. Some make a further effort, and announce the plots on their website. Again you are up against the unwritten rules that say that, if an architect finds a plot of land for a developer, they will either get a finder's fee, or the commission to design the house. You could make a similar offer, but a developer will not have the same concerns about their design that a family will have, so you may not wish to be denied your choice of architect in this way. Architects may also be a useful source of initial advice about a site, and may be able to tell you at an early stage whether or not your ideas are realistic.

If you find a plot that no-one else knows about, be very careful who you tell. Regardless of codes of conduct, 'money talks', so only tell those professionals that you know you can trust, and don't reveal the location of a site to anyone unless it is essential.

Solicitors

Another professional who is almost certain to be involved in the sale of a site is a solicitor. They may be helping a family or company manage their property portfolio, or be instructed to arrange the disposal of a property with development potential on behalf of the executors of a will. The latter usually prefer a swift, no-nonsense sale for a quick return, to more drawn-out negotiations.

Builders

Builders are not your natural allies when it comes to finding land, more your competitors. But there are some circumstances in which they may want to help you. Sometimes a small builder will not want the risk of developing a site, perhaps because of cash-flow problems, and may be prepared to sell you something from their 'land bank'. They will, however, usually add a condition that you have to use them to build the new house. This is a serious drawback, because if you agree to it before you have detailed plans and specifications you will find that the construction cost is very high, and every extra above the standard requirements may be charged at a high rate.

Land Finders

Large developers use professional land finders, who can sometimes be found in the Yellow Pages. But there is an economy of scale for big sites, because they can take the same time to find as a small one like the one you are looking for. So don't expect much help from this quarter, unless you agree to pay a significant percentage of the land price in commission. Even if you agree to this, they may find a lot of good sites which are suitable for building a house on and making a profit, but which may not suit your particular requirements.

Self-Build Development Companies

There are a few companies, some connected to kit suppliers or builders, who buy up larger sites, split them into individual properties, and sell them on to self builders. Check whether you are tied into using a particular firm if you buy a plot. If this is the only way you can get a site in the right area, make sure that you get independent expert advice before signing on the dotted line.

NEVER buy a plot without planning approval unless you have made a realistic assessment of the risk of not getting it, and can afford to lose your money painlessly.

The 'Land with Prospects' Trap

There are a few people prepared to exploit desperate, unworldly plot hunters and relieve them of their money, for maximum profit and minimum outlay. These companies offer what are apparently prime potential plots, for a bargain price. The catch is that there is no planning approval. It is suggested that, in the fullness of time, the land may eventually get planning approval, and you will then own a prime building plot. The truth is usually that although the land may get approval one day, it probably never will, and you have wasted your money. If you are considering taking up one of these offers get independent advice first, regardless of how attractive it seems.

There is a huge army of seasoned experts out looking for 'the real thing', backed by big money from developers who will risk significant capital to acquire the rights to future development land long before it becomes available – sometimes decades in advance. The hard truth is that these bona fide organisations are not going to sell this land to you, but will build their own housing development, because the profit is far bigger. If anyone offers you a bargain plot, unless they are a generous relative, think again.

This site was being advertised by the owner without using an estate agent. A family, who saw the board as they drove past, bought it and built a large five-bedroom house.

Proactive

If you find sitting around waiting for other people to help you get your plot frustrating and fruitless, you are not alone; most people in your position feel the same. But there is more that you can do, if you have the time and inclination. All the methods listed below have been used successfully.

Scouting for a Site

After you have identified some particular villages, suburbs, or streets that fit your requirements, you can make yourself acquainted with them, and get some healthy exercise at the same time.

If you want to find a potential site that no-one has thought of selling yet, there are several rules to follow:

1. Select a few key areas, for instance two or three villages or areas of a town. Limit your search to these key areas, in order to ensure that you cover them thoroughly.

2. Buy a map that shows houses; for instance, OS Pathfinders show houses at 1:25,000. You will be able to use this map to record where potential plots are.

3. Walk around your chosen areas, since, if you drive, you may miss the less-obvious sites.

4. Methodically take details of sites. Note the address, location and size. Take photographs if possible, and draw sketch plans. These details will help you to remember which site is which, after you have visited several one after the other.

5. Deliver standard letters to houses adjacent to potential building land, asking the owner to contact you if they are interested in selling. Always be polite and never be 'pushy' – people are often suspicious of anyone who makes this kind of approach.

6. Talk to locals. Visit the local pubs and shops, and ask if anyone knows of any land for sale. If anybody seems helpful, leave a contact address or telephone number.

What to Look For

When you are out scouting an area, you can train yourself to spot opportunities. Once you start thinking like this, it can be difficult to stop, and a walk through a village while you are on holiday will never be the same again – potential building plots loom up on every road. These are some of the clues that you should look for. If you want to follow up with some more detailed site investigation, go to the 'Assessing a Site' section of this book:

1. Large gaps between and behind houses. It is usually easier to get planning approval for development in between, or next to, existing houses. If there is space beside a house, and especially if it has easy access to the road, it is a potential plot. If there is a big back garden, and access for vehicles to get to it down the side of the house, it may be possible to build at the bottom of it.

2. Narrow gaps that are not overlooked. Sometimes sites that are apparently too narrow can be used to squeeze in a small house, provided that the access or windows of the houses either side are not affected – it is just possible to build a detached house only 5 or 6 m wide.

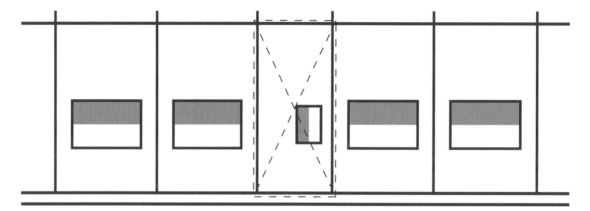

An ideal infill site: part of someone's garden with a garage on it. Good frontage, existing road access, space for a house to be built similar to surrounding buildings, no overlooking neighbours.

3. Look for houses of a similar size and quality to the one you wish to build. The way that houses are valued means that it is less economic to develop a house that is massively disproportionate to those surrounding it. You can end up over-developing, that is spending far more money on a house than you could ever sell it for; or under-developing, that is building too small a house and failing to realise the full potential of the site.

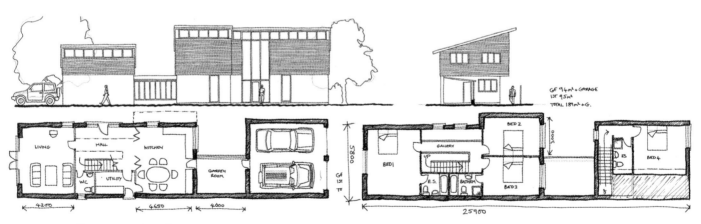

House on a narrow site.

4. Demolition opportunities. Small bungalows on large sites, run-down houses, and detached council properties on generous pre-war sites all have the potential to become your plot.

5. Vehicle access. Whatever land you find, unless it is near a city or town centre, will have to have space to park, so there must be a way of reaching it by car.

6. Disused land and brownfield sites. These are very easy to miss. It takes a lot of imagination to see a petrol-filling station, a telephone exchange, a disused industrial unit, or a scrapyard as the site for a beautiful home, but they all could be, subject to planning approval.

Unlikely site: once cleared of buildings and other clutter, this plot will make an excellent site for a small detached house.

7. Site assembly. If you see a number of gardens that are too small for a house, but together could be big enough, take a leaf from the professional developer's book and consider assembling your own site. It needs tact, patience, and a bit of business acumen, but it has been done – particularly when the homeowners realise that a small bit of their garden can earn them some money. Backland developments can be assembled in this way (see diagram below).

8. Estate agent boards. While you are out and about, make a careful note of which agents have the most signboards up in an area. This gives useful guidance as to which of them is likely to know about land for sale.

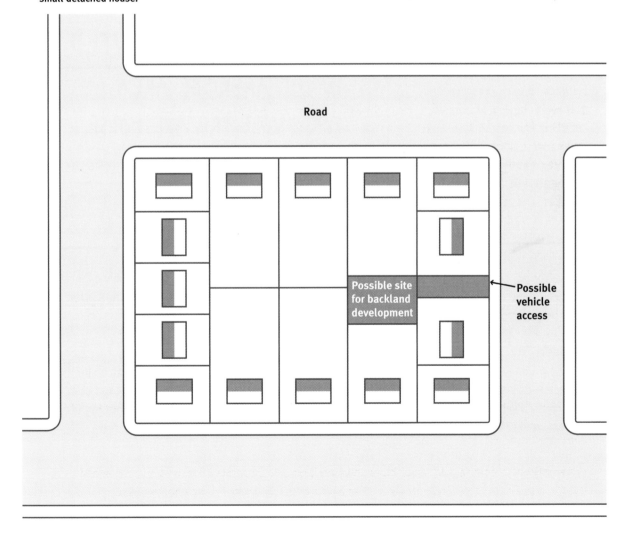

Backland Development.

Major Landowners/Estate Departments

There are all sorts of institutions, organisations and companies that own land and sell some off periodically – they include the railway management body, universities, traditional landowners like the Duchy of Cornwall, the coal authority, and district and county councils. It is a long process contacting all of them, but if you can keep abreast of the local and regional news, you may discover one of them is offering parcels of land.

Farmers

Farmers own so much land that they sometimes forget that some of it can be developed. There are few ways around agricultural ties, which mean that a property can only be lived in if the occupants earn their main living off the surrounding land. But occasionally, farmers get approval to build a house on a separate plot, perhaps with the idea that a relative will build on it. If this doesn't happen, the approval may be renewed regularly until they decide what to do. Most farmers are listed in the Yellow Pages.

Never phone a farmer after early evening. They generally rise very early and go to bed very early, and will not appreciate being disturbed.

Post Office

There are a shrinking number of sub-post offices, but every area, especially in the countryside, has a corner shop or general store that everyone visits for basic supplies. The cost of a postcard-sized advert is a few pence a week, and these are good places to advertise if you are looking for a plot of land in the area.

BUILDING PLOT WANTED

IN THE AMBRIDGE AREA FOR SINGLE PRIVATE HOUSE GOOD PRICE PAID.

TEL: 0115 543210

Suggested postcard for sub-post office/corner shop.

Advertising

Apart from checking the local papers for adverts for land, it may be worth putting in your own advert. This is potentially expensive because, to be effective, it will have to stay in for at least several weeks, but it is a method often used by developers.

Finder's Fee

Finally, you may also wish to consider offering a finder's fee for anyone who leads you to a site that you eventually build on. This will have to be a significant amount to be attractive, but if you are looking for a valuable site and intend to build a large house and hope to earn some profit in the process, it may be worth the investment.

Design and Planning

Once you have found what looks like the right place to build your home, you must move quickly to acquire the site. Hopefully, you will not have to purchase the site before you and your professional advisors carry out the basic checks on the plot and its surroundings, which are listed at the start of this section. Having procured your site, the design process can start in earnest, and the real fun can begin. You have to find a designer that you can work with, prepare a design together that suits your requirements, and persuade the local authority planners that it will be acceptable. From this point onwards, more and more people will start to get involved in the process. Some you can choose. Others will have some control over the destiny of your project whether you like it or not, and you will have to find a way to work with them.

Summary of This Stage:

- Assessing a Site
- Buying a Plot
- Finding a Designer
- Designing your House
- Getting Planning Permission

Assessing a Site

Once you have found a potential site for your new home, it should be examined to reveal the benefits and disadvantages it offers to your project. Your first question should be: 'Why has it not been built on before?' Don't relax until you have a full answer. It is tempting to rush the analysis of the site, particularly if the vendor wants a quick sale and has alternative buyers waiting. Sometimes it will not be possible to wait for all the necessary checks to be carried out, but try to complete as many as is practical. You can't remove the chance of site-related problems surfacing

This picture shows a typical site in the garden of a private house, staked out to identify the boundaries.

later on, but by the time you 'sign on the dotted line' you should have identified the risk you are taking, by making a list of unanswered questions. You can photocopy the site checklist at the end of this section to investigate a plot when you find one.

Initial Appraisal

Typically, the initial information available concerns the expected sale price, the size of the plot, and its location. To make the decision to go further, you need to have some background knowledge of the locality and to have an idea of what a house like yours would be worth once built. You also need to know the minimum plot size required, and whether there will be enough money left in your budget to complete your project after the land purchase. For most of the UK, the rule of thumb which says that land should cost between one third and a half of your total investment should help you in completing some back-of-the-envelope calculations (see the earlier section on 'Preparing a Budget'). However, this calculation does not stand up in areas where the housing market is distorted by severe shortage, such as the Southeast of England, where the land value may be disproportionate to the build cost. Most self builders take a few months acquiring some knowledge of the local market before they feel confident enough to start making serious offers.

The First Visit

When first visiting a potential building plot, some people find it hard to visualise how the site might look with a completed property on it. Empty land can look deceptively small, until the rough dimensions of a building footprint have been paced out. You must be sure that your house is likely to fit in the space available, and an Ordnance Survey (OS) map at 1:1,250 scale is a useful aid to finding this out. OS maps are surprisingly accurate, and show lots of useful information about the site and its relationship to the surroundings. They are sometimes issued with the agent's details. If not, they can be obtained either from the local planning department or an OS agency for a reasonable cost.

Find out the postcode of the site early. This makes information on it easier to find, particularly from local and statutory authorities.

Land which is overgrown and derelict, or has an existing building already on it, or is covered in tarmac, may not look inspiring at first glance, but this is a time to use your imagination. What would the surroundings look like if an eyesore is removed? What would you see through your bedroom window? Make a quick run through the 'Site Checklist', at the end of this section, and see how many questions can be dealt with on the spot.

Always take a camera with you to record as much of the site as possible. It is surprising how easy it is to forget the detail of your dream site. Take as many photos as are needed to fully record the site and its surroundings. Unless the plot is on your doorstep, the cost of a few prints far outweighs the time lost if you have to go back to a site to reassure your faulty memory. Back up the photos with a rough sketch, annotated with key information such as boundary conditions and manhole locations.

Take different-coloured pens to do the site survey, and plenty of biros which will not run if it rains.

Once on site, check the boundaries carefully and make sure that it is clear what is included in the site. If the site is marked out with timber stakes hammered into the ground, take some quick check dimensions. Read through the agent's details to see if the description matches the reality.

Detailed Site Investigation

Once an offer for a plot has been accepted by the vendor, it is time to start examining in earnest the site you are about to own. To do this thoroughly, you will have to invest time and money, and get expert assistance. A diligent site appraisal is vital to the success of any development, and is as much about ruling problems out as it is about identifying them.

Site Surveys
Land Surveyor

Sometimes it is suggested that an OS map plus a few check dimensions taken on site are all that is needed to draw up a design and submit for planning, thus saving the cost of a proper measured survey of the site, or at least putting it off until later in the development process. This is a false economy. Once you have an accurate drawing of the site and its immediate surroundings, you can clarify exactly what you are buying, and ensure that the planning application is accurate. Get the size or shape wrong and you could keep your solicitor busy arguing with neighbours for many years after you have moved in. Get the planning application drawing wrong and your permission could be declared invalid after you have started building and the errors come to light.

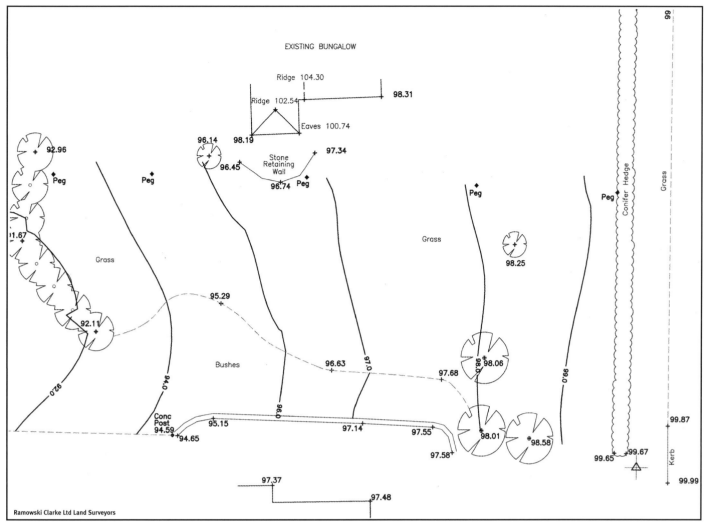

An example of a typical site survey, which accurately locates boundaries, major features and levels.

A simple site survey can be a 'DIY job' for those with a little experience or a practical mind. Any site which has significant level changes, is an irregular shape, has natural features, such as trees, which are to be retained or has obstacles that will remain on site close to the house footprint, must be surveyed by someone with expertise. That usually means an architect or land surveyor. The latter specialists use modern equipment such as lasers and computers to plot accurate plans and sections of an area of land. With bigger projects, and engineering works such as roads, they will also 'set out' and tie the new structure into the survey drawings.

A typical site survey will include:

- north point
- existing boundaries and their type, e.g. fence, ditch, hedge, etc.
- levels in and around the site, to a fixed datum
- existing buildings adjacent to the site
- adjacent roads, pavements and footpaths
- trees and significant vegetation
- manholes
- any features, e.g. rock outcrop, pits, ponds, spoil heaps, etc.

Architect

The architect will usually get involved at this stage, to carry out checks on each aspect of the site. Any designer worth their salt will want to visit the site and spend a little time getting to know it before preparing sketch proposals. Someone with knowledge of the whole design and construction process will know what to look for, and will quickly identify many of the benefits and burdens the site will offer.

The Solicitor

Solicitors will be involved in a similar way to a normal house purchase, checking the deeds for legal restrictions and carrying out a search to verify any information available from the local and statutory authorities. The one thing that solicitors rarely do is visit the site, and the purchase of small parcels of land is relatively rare compared to their regular house-conveyancing work. Consequently, any work done by your legal advisor must be supplemented by other site investigations (by yourself or your architect), and all doubts should be raised and pursued until you are satisfied.

The Planning Officer

Always contact the planning department at an early stage in a site investigation. Assuming an approval is in place, try to talk to the officer who actually handled the original application. If this person is not available, talk to whoever is most likely to be dealing with any further applications on the site, and ask to see the planning file if you are not confident that they are giving the whole story.

The Building Control Officer

These professionals spend a lot of time looking down holes in the ground, as they inspect nearly all the building projects in their area. Usually there are some building control officers who have worked in the area for many years. They are the best experts you will find on local ground conditions. They are usually happy to give you the benefit of their experience, and a single telephone call asking for advice could save a lot of time.

Planning Issues

Ideally the planning status of a potential plot for your new home should be checked before you even make a visit. But, even if there is definitely an approval in place, there is a lot more that you need to find out before you make an offer. It may be possible to build a house of some sort on the plot, but can you build your house, as opposed to any other design?

Planning Approval

Land should not be finally purchased until some form of planning approval has been granted. Descriptions such as 'potential building plot' should be treated with great caution, since any vendor being properly advised would get the approval in place before putting it on the market, to maximise its value. The process of obtaining planning approval is dealt with in later sections of this book. At this stage, a copy of the complete Planning Approval Notice for the site should be acquired. Check that it is the entire document, including any conditions. Agents and vendors are surprisingly lax at providing this information, occasionally because its reveals some unfavourable restrictions. Check whether it gives outline or detailed approval, and the date that it was granted. Also check that the approval applies to the whole site and the correct address – this is easily done by asking to see the OS map, with the relevant areas marked in red ink, which must be submitted with every application.

Outline planning permission ('OPP') is mainly concerned with the use of the site, not the detail of the design. Sometimes limited details that are considered crucial to the permission are included, such as the vehicle access design. OPP is valid for three years, and approval of the detailed design must be applied for before this time limit expires. Once approval has been granted for the outstanding details, you have two years to start work, or five years from the date of the original OPP approval, whichever is the longer. After this date, if the details have not been submitted, the planning permission expires, and a reapplication will be needed.

Full planning approval ('FPP') includes a description of the size, shape, external appearance and plans of the proposal. If you are interested in a site with FPP, find out why it was obtained. It is more expensive to obtain than outline approval, and unnecessary if the vendor has always intended to sell the plot on. One reason may be that the local authority insisted on it. Just because a plot has a full approval it doesn't necessarily mean that you have to build that design, but, if the planners have insisted on a detailed design it suggests they are looking for a high degree of control, and it may be tricky to get approval for any significant modifications. For example, most local authorities will no longer grant OPP for one-off houses in a Conservation Area.

However, at the time of writing, the government is has approved proposals to reduce the five years for which full permission is active down to three years.

Don't assume that because an approval has been granted on a site in the past, it will automatically get approval again after it has expired. If the Local Plan policies have changed with respect to that plot, it could be refused.

The Local Plan

The Local Plan acts as a 'bible' for planners, and will list the guidelines and standards they work to. If your proposals are likely to conflict with it, be ready for a fight with the local authority. Every five years or so, all district and metropolitan councils produce a comprehensive set of documents which describe their planning policies in detail. These Local Plans go through an exhaustive process of development, involving submissions from all interested bodies as well as the general public and their elected representatives. The end result is difficult to challenge, and its policies will be vigorously defended by planning officers. Before granting or rejecting any planning application, it is checked against the Local Plan for the area. If an application is rejected, the planning authority should refer back to the Local Plan and demonstrate how the application contravenes it. Sometimes the specific clauses that have been breached are stated in the refusal notice.

This would all be relatively simple, except that as a Local Plan matures towards the end of its term, a replacement 'Draft Plan' will be in preparation, which gradually becomes more influential as it passes through each stage of public scrutiny.

The Local Plan should also be checked for information on possible future developments adjacent to the site. If there is about to be a new road, housing estate or industrial shed on the doorstep, the warning can usually be found there. At the time of writing, the Government is proposing to change this system and replace Local Plans with regionally created Strategic Plans which will perform the same function.

Relationship to adjoining buildings – privacy and amenity

Almost all plots are close enough to other buildings to affect existing residents. A proposal that intrudes into a neighbour's private space, or is detrimental to their quality of life, will meet with resistance. Assuming that there are houses close to the site, the planners will be concerned not only with the effect of a new house on the privacy of the neighbours, but also that the level of privacy of the new house will be acceptable. This means that if a site is overlooked by several properties close

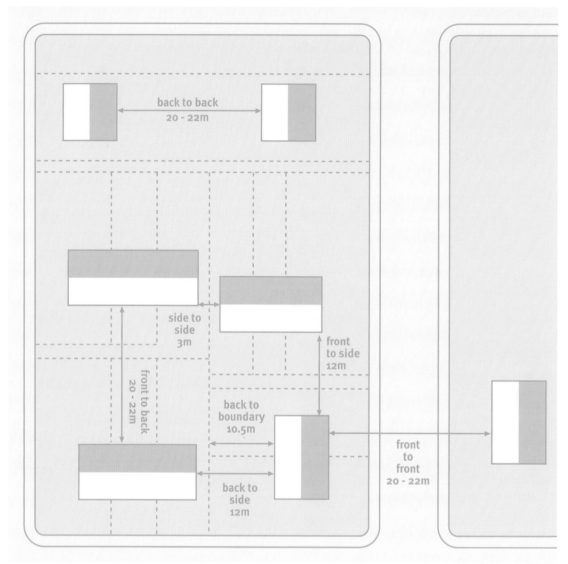

Typical spacing between houses required by planners.

to the boundary front and back, the design will be restricted. The planners often set minimum distances between houses, particularly where windows to the main rooms are concerned.

This is one reason most standard house designs built by developers, which tend to fill the plot close to either side of the boundary, have no significant windows facing the neighbouring plots. Bathroom windows that are in obscured glass are usually acceptable, because it is not easy to see through them into your neighbours' windows, and vice versa.

Increasing pressure from the government for more housing means that planners sometimes relax these spacing distances, especially in urban areas.

Planners are also fond of talking about the effects of new developments on the 'amenity' of their neighbours. What they mean is the right of people to relax and enjoy living in their home. There are no automatic rights to light or sunlight, for example, but if a proposed house would significantly reduce these for the surrounding families, the planners have grounds for refusing to grant approval.

Building Lines

Planning policy may prevent a new house from being built further forward than the others on a road. Often in a suburban street, the front elevations of the houses are all in line on each side of the road. Where a site is an infill plot (i.e. a gap between a row of houses on a street), the planners are likely to prevent the new house projecting very far forward from what they call a 'building line'.

Relationship to adjoining buildings – Context and Precedent

The character of an area will influence the style, size and massing of any development. As part of the site investigation, look closely at the surrounding streetscape. The new building will have to react to the design of the other buildings adjacent to the plot and in the surrounding area. The design may either be 'in keeping' or a deliberate contrast, but the context should be studied and respected either way. There are also valuable clues as to what has been acceptable to the planning authority in the past, in the form of recently constructed buildings and extensions.

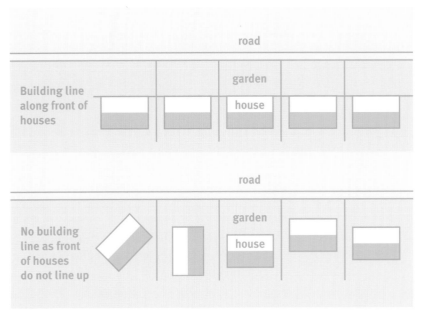

If the fronts of a row of houses are in line, the planners may impose a 'building line'.

Study the character of local traditional buildings.

Land Use

The designated use of a site may affect its value and development options. It sometimes comes as a surprise to newcomers to the planning process, but planning departments are just as concerned with the use of a piece of land as they are about what is built on it. This can lead to some anomalies, such as an ugly, decaying industrial building being left to rot because the planners will not grant a change of use until they are absolutely sure that it will not be able to provide employment for local people.

The use of land in the UK is carefully controlled, and often a politically sensitive subject because when land uses are changed, the local community is always affected to a greater or lesser degree. For example, a housing estate replacing an industrial building will lead to different patterns of traffic flow through an area. Property prices are affected, but there is also a reduction in the potential for an area to provide local employment. If you plan to work from home, and your business is of a type that affects the character of the area, you will need planning permission for part of your house to be used in this way. For example, if a physiotherapist sees clients at home, or if staff are employed beyond immediate family, both these will generate vehicle traffic and probably require specific approval. If approval is not applied for, sooner or later a neighbour will complain, and an enforcement officer will come knocking on your door.

New house are regularly built in the gardens of existing houses in villages, a process which is described in planning terms as 'intensification of use'. In a small settlement, even the addition of a single property can have an adverse impact on neighbouring houses, and the planners may refuse permission for this reason.

Green belts

Some of the most hotly contested planning disputes for self builders centre on a local authority's green-belt policy (if it has one). First established in the 1940s, green belts are used by planning authorities as a way of containing development around existing towns, villages and suburbs – encouraged by country-dwellers who wish to preserve their rural idyll. The system can, however, lead to some absurd anomalies: for instance, a local authority may happily draft the Local Plan to allow several thousand houses to swallow up large areas of agricultural land, but deny approval to someone who wishes to build a modest house, or even add to an existing home.

If a house is to be demolished and replaced in a green-belt area, planning approval is normally possible, but usually the new house is restricted in size. The extent of this restriction varies between local authorities, but a typical allowance is an increase of 50 per cent, by volume, over and above the size of the existing house.

A classic hitch caused by green-belt policy arises when a plot is offered for sale as part-garden and part-paddock. Close study of the planning permission reveals that only the garden has approval, and the paddock is excluded, being beyond the red line on the OS map submitted with the application. The paddock cannot be turned into garden in this situation, because the use could have been changed without planning approval and it is still considered by the planners to be a field. So the actual building plot is far smaller than it seems at first glance. The planners are very inflexible on this point. To them, the difference between a meadow and a lawn is huge. Householders who have innocently enlarged their back gardens by planting flower beds on agricultural land may be forced to return the land to its original state – if they are found out.

Conservation Areas and Listed Buildings

If a site is in a Conservation Area, or close to a listed building or structure, planners can insist on the use of better-than-usual quality materials, and many designs will be deemed unacceptable. These tight restrictions are likely to push up the development cost.

Conservation Areas

A vendor should know if their plot is in a Conservation Area, but if they were to choose not to advertise the fact, it should be picked up in the solicitor's search. Conservation Areas are designated by the local authority where they feel there is a particular character or historical significance to a locality that should be preserved. The character of an area is defined by its streets, boundary walls and trees, as well as actual buildings, and so these are usually protected in some way as well. This is achieved by designating a Conservation Area and issuing an 'Article 4 Direction', which removes the usual rights available to householders to make minor adjustments to the outside of their homes without making formal applications for approval.

Obtaining planning approval in a Conservation Area is harder than is normally the case, and the wider local community take far more interest in what is being proposed. Apart from requiring a higher standard of design and construction, the local authority will usually consult local history societies and other interested groups for their opinions. Many councils employ conservation officers, whose job is to offer advice to the relevant case officer on what is acceptable. In reality, the conservation officer usually has the final say as to whether or not a design in a Conservation Area will receive a recommendation for approval. The effect of this is that the assessment of a design made by the council becomes rather subjective, and all but the most enlightened planning departments resist anything that is not 'in keeping' with the area. In fact, the government stipulates that new development must preserve or enhance the Conservation Area, and does not expressly rule out a well-designed modern building provided that it does this.

Any significant demolition work will require an application for Conservation Area Consent to be made and approved beforehand. All trees within the designated boundary effectively have a Tree Preservation Order in place (see 'Tree Preservation Order' section, later).

The greatest advantage of building a new home in a Conservation Area is that once you've moved in, you can be reasonably confident that the area will be protected from too many other people doing the same.

Conservation Areas are used by planners to prevent buildings spoiling the character of an area. The red roof was added to this row of houses before the area had protection.

Listed Buildings

A vendor will not necessarily know that nearby buildings have been listed. Sometimes quite modern buildings are included, although if a building is over about 150 years old and not significantly altered, listing is very likely. Proximity to a listed building will elicit similar rigorous requirements from the planning officer to those of a Conservation Area. This applies especially if the proposal and the listed property can be viewed together, or the former is prominent when looking out from the latter. When a building is listed, all the adjoining land in the same ownership at the time is included, so all structures within this curtilage are covered. Sometimes this includes relatively modern, unremarkable buildings, statues, boundary walls and outbuildings in a poor state of repair. To alter any of them without listed building consent is a criminal offence, which carries a heavy fine.

There are three official levels of listing in England and Wales: Grade I, Grade II*, and Grade II. Grade I is the most important category, covering buildings of national importance, Grade II is for buildings of local importance and Grade II* is between the two. The main effect of the listing is the level of scrutiny that any application attracts. In England and Wales, any building work close to a listed property will attract the attention of either English Heritage or Cadw (the Welsh equivalent). In Scotland, instead of listing, buildings are designated Category A, Category B or Category C(S) and monitored by Historic Scotland. In Northern Ireland, the Environment and Heritage Service performs the role, using Grade A, Grade B, Grade B1 and Grade B2 to rank the importance of the Province's historic buildings.

Preliminary enquiries to the planning officer will usually reveal any problem in this area.

If you build near a prominent listed building, there will be more planning constraints.

Ancient Monuments and Archaeological Areas

Assuming that you are not going to try building next to Stonehenge, the main concern will be to check whether the plot is in an area of ancient settlement now no longer visible from ground level. Once the council have decided that an area may have archaeological importance, it can place restrictions in connection with a planning approval. The first, and easiest to cope with is called a 'watching brief'. This means that when excavations are carried out, you pay an archaeologist to check, by looking into holes and trenches, that there are no artifacts to be recovered, or structures to record. The second, more onerous and expensive, requirement is for a ground investigation to be carried out before approval is granted, usually by digging trenches or holes as stipulated by the archaeologist. So the days of hurriedly pouring concrete over suspiciously ancient-looking pottery, to avoid delays to a building project, are over.

This tree on a plot for a house is protected, but also forms an attractive screen, improving privacy.

Tree Preservation Orders (TPOs)

If some or all of the trees on a plot have TPOs on them, they may restrict the footprint of a building, particularly in clay areas, where the foundations are affected (see 'Ground Conditions', later). Councils can use TPOs to protect either individual trees, a group of them, or all the trees in a given area. They can also issue provisional TPOs very quickly, to prevent a landowner removing trees before they are protected. Any intentional damage or significant pruning is a criminal offence. It is a good idea to try to incorporate trees into a design, but sadly it is usual to fell any trees that would prevent the house being built as soon as possible, to reduce the risk of TPOs being put in place. If a landowner senses an imminent TPO, the felling is often carried out over a weekend, to reduce the chance of the council spotting what is going on and issuing a provisional TPO.

National Parks

In an area designated by the government as a National Park, the National Parks Authority deals with most planning issues. These bodies have a particular interest in maintaining public access to the countryside and its footpaths and bridleways, and in the conservation of natural beauty. They have stated policies regarding new developments, and will oppose anything that they feel is not in accordance with them. The implications for anyone hoping to build a house in one of these areas is that the proposal is often quite difficult to justify. A much higher standard of design and construction is required, and should be backed up by good quality drawings. This will inevitably lead to extra costs.

Once a property is built, permitted development rights are restricted in a similar fashion to those in a Conservation Area. The Norfolk and Suffolk Broads are run in a similar way – although the area is not, strictly speaking, a National Park.

Areas of Outstanding Natural Beauty

These areas have similar restrictions to National Parks, but are far smaller in area.

Sites of Special Scientific Interest (SSSI)

These areas, which can be as small as a single field, have been designated by the relevant government agency for each part of the UK as having flora, fauna or geological features which are of national or international importance. English Nature, the Countryside Council for Wales, and Scottish Natural Heritage cover their respective countries, and the Environment and Heritage Service covers Northern Ireland in this respect. If approval has been granted for a new house to be built near to such a site (as opposed to within the site, which is unlikely), conditions may be imposed to limit the risk of any harm to the SSSI.

Protected Species

Certain animal species are protected by law, in that it is an offence to disturb them. Bats roost in derelict buildings, and approval is necessary before carrying out any work that will affect them. If the bats are known about, English Nature (or their local counterpart) will be consulted by the local authority. Other creatures with this level of protection are owls, badgers and newts. Their presence in an area may prevent any development taking place at all, or severely affect the time of year that work can be carried out.

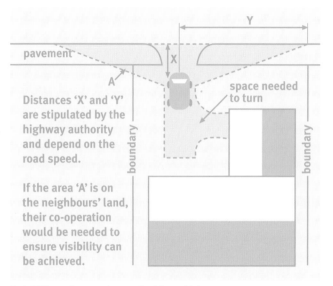

Distances 'X' and 'Y' are stipulated by the highway authority and depend on the road speed.

If the area 'A' is on the neighbours' land, their co-operation would be needed to ensure visibility can be achieved.

A visibility splay may be required for vehicles leaving a site.

Highways

Most new houses need on-site parking in some form, so there must be space to fit in a driveway or garage along with the rest of the house. Vehicles will be moving on and off the site once the house is occupied, and this must be done safely. The highways officer is usually consulted as part of the planning process, and may lay down requirements for the site. Where the road is busy, highways officers are particularly concerned to ensure that cars can leave the plot in forward gear, and that as the car pulls out on to the road, the driver has clear visibility in both directions. This is indicated by two triangles of land either side of the site entry, which must be kept clear of obstructions. The point to note is that one of these triangles may cut across someone else's land. If it does, and the owner of that land will either not agree to ensure that visibility is maintained, or to sell the land, then it may be impossible to develop the plot.

This access to a potential plot has no pavement and poor visibility. Consequently, it may not be possible to build here at all.

Controversy

In theory, planners should not refuse a design simply because it is not 'in keeping' with the houses next door. In reality, if you want a striking design, there may be opposition from several quarters. Unusual designs seem to be more acceptable on urban sites, but can enhance the countryside as well, if they are of sufficient quality. If you want a modern design, a lot of preparatory work will be necessary, working with the planners and the local community.

Climate and Environmental Features
The Sun

Even if two sites are identical in size, shape and form, the way a house is designed on them may be entirely different if the sun falls on them from different directions, or if features around the perimeters cause shading in different ways. Depending on the way that each room is used, they will benefit from the sun at different times of the day (see the earlier 'Lifestyle' section). Keen gardeners will want to make the best use of sunlight for their plants. If the combination of house, garden, shade, and direction of the sun is unfavourable, it may be a reason to reject a site at an early stage.

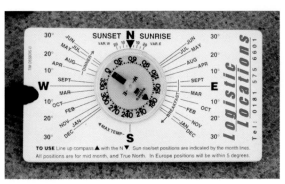

This sunfinding compass is used by photographers to predict which direction the sun will come from at different times of the year. You can use it on site, or with an orientated site plan, to work out how much sun you will get.

Make sure you note the time of year and weather conditions when you visit the site. Try to see it under different conditions, especially when wet and windy.

Exposure

A site that has unprotected sides exposed to large areas of open land around it, will experience stronger winds than a sheltered plot. The exposure level is also dependent on which part of the country the site is in. Wind speed has been measured nationally, and different parts of the country are classified accordingly. For example, Newcastle has a higher 'gust' wind speed than London. In extreme cases, such as on top of cliffs or escarpments, the Building Regulations limit the proportions of a building. But even in more normal situations, the wind speed will affect the fixings of roof tiles (to avoid them being blown off) and the wall construction ('full-fill' cavity walls – i.e. those in which insulation fills the entire cavity, leaving no air gap – may fail in driving rain; construction and cavity-tray design must therefore be of high quality).

The effects of wind can be moderated by planting fast-growing trees, or by designing both building and landscape to provide shelter.

Levels

Totally level sites are rare – most have some kind of fall across them. Sometimes the change in level across the land looks deceptively shallow, particularly if there are no reference points, like a horizontal garden wall or buildings close by. If the ground is poorly drained, surface water will have to be directed away from the new house. If the levels change in relation to neighbouring plots, planning issues such as overlooking will be exacerbated.

Sudden or extreme changes in level indicate either a local change in the subsoil geology, or, more likely, hidden features or made-up ground (see 'Ground Conditions' section, later).

All types of ground have a natural angle, called the 'angle of repose', to which they will return if left. To avoid this angle being exceeded on a sloping site, substantial retaining walls may have to be built, which represent a significant cost. If the ground is dug into and cannot be disposed of on site, extra tipping charges will be incurred – again, adding to expenditure. These additional costs should be assessed when deciding on the price to offer for the plot. Another risk is that the ground stability is poor, which, without proper design of the foundations, can result in landslip. This may already have occurred on the site, and might be indicated by the tilting of walls or trees.

But it is precisely when the level changes are more dramatic that one-off house designs come into their own. Such sites are often rejected by builders and developers, who are looking for easier options. A developer may even factor-in the cost of levelling a sloping site to provide a flat base on which to build a conventional house, when a more creative solution – using the slope to generate the design – is actually cheaper to build.

Access

Some sites can only be reached by a long drive or track, or up a steep slope, making access difficult. If the path is unroadworthy and has to be made up with tarmac or a similar surface, the cost can be significant. If access prevents any delivery lorries getting to the site, either the contractor's cost will rise, as everything has to be moved manually, or you will have a long, back-breaking job doing it yourself. If the access road is longer than 20 metres, the building control officer may ask for space to be provided within the site for a fire engine to turn.

This house exploits the steep slope as a feature of its design.

Flooding

Thanks to global warming, the risk of flooding is increasing annually. Proximity to the sea, a river, canal or other watercourse would suggest a flooding risk. Serious flooding risks are usually flagged up by the local authority at planning stage, but it is simple enough to obtain an OS map of the area that locates nearby sources of water, as well as contours. If an area is prone to flooding, the building can be built further above ground level than normal (possibly leading to a subsequent conflict with the building control officer over level access). The structure should be designed to be water resistant, e.g. with concrete ground floors, no basements, continuous damp proofing, minimal use of timber at low level, and water-resistant floor coverings (e.g. vinyl rather than carpet). In particularly prone areas, pumps and special drainage may be necessary.

The depth at which the ground is saturated can vary seasonally, so that what appears to be a dry site in summer may be flooded in winter, as the water table rises. Even if the water table remains below the surface, if it is above foundation depth it may be impossible to achieve watertightness using conventional construction methods, and piling might be required – especially if the ground is poorly consolidated.

Water movements below ground can also introduce or concentrate pollutants below the site.

Buildings close to water, or where there is a high water table, need to be designed on the assumption that they will flood.

Noise

Noise can be difficult to assess, especially if the site is visited briefly during working hours, when you unconsciously filter out normal background noise like traffic. Try to visit the site at a weekend, and at different times of the day. Close your eyes and listen. This way you will pick up any unusual background sounds, such as factories, farm machinery, etc. It may be down to chance if you pick up intermittent noise, such as aeroplanes or land with seasonal shooting rights, but local maps can provide clues.

The best way to effectively reduce intrusive sound is by mass, or dead weight. If there is an identifiable noise coming from one direction, such as traffic sounds, it is possible to design so that the bedrooms are on the side of the house furthest away from it, using the mass of the building itself to provide sound insulation. If there is room on the site, bund walls can be created as part of the landscaping. Contrary to popular belief, a row of trees is useless at significantly reducing noise. At best they can only screen the source from view.

Environmental Pollution

Pollution is a fact of 21st-century life. Sources include factories, roads and crop-spraying. Apart from rejecting sites in the vicinity of obvious sources of pollution, there is little that can be done, other than installing mechanical ventilation with filtration units, which will be of limited benefit. Historical pollution can lead to contaminated ground (see 'Contaminated Land' section, later).

Trees and Natural Vegetation

Trees may affect the foundations of a building (dealt with in 'Clay and Trees' section, later), sun penetration on to the site, and exposure – but are also a natural resource which can be exploited by the house design, perhaps by arranging the footprint in order to retain them without detriment to the building.

Japanese Knotweed is a different prospect altogether. More prevalent in Wales and Southwest England, it is a fast-growing weed, which is also strong enough to damage buildings. If the plant is present on a site, it is essential to control it (complete eradication is not easy), and this usually means the use of a pesticide, as well as regular weeding. If the site is near a watercourse, the National Rivers Authority should be informed of any plans for chemical treatment.

Radon

Radon gas is invisible, and has no odour. It occurs naturally underground, is radioactive and seeps through into buildings, where it can build up over time in poorly ventilated areas. In parts of the country where levels are relatively high, it has been linked to health problems such as lung cancer. Some of the higher-risk areas are Cornwall, Devon, Derbyshire and Northamptonshire. New houses built in these locations have had to install protection measures for some time, but in 1999 the number of areas considered at risk was increased – to include areas such as the Yorkshire Dales, parts of Wales, north Oxfordshire and parts of the Midlands.

Radon-protection measures include installing a continuous damp-proof membrane and creating a sump under the building, which is then ventilated out of harm's way. In areas at risk from radon, the local authority Building Control Department will ask either for protection measures or for a certificate from the British Geological Society confirming that the site is low risk.

Coastal Erosion

Any imminent coastal erosion should be immediately obvious, but the long-term situation should also be assessed if a site is close to sea cliffs.

Ground Conditions

Subsoil Type

The subsoil is the layer, immediately below the topsoil, in which the walls will be founded. Consequently, its nature will have a direct influence on the design and cost of the foundations. The simplest method of identifying this is to dig some holes. The subsoil's bearing capacity varies with different types of ground, and will affect the design and complexity of the foundations needed to support a building. In most cases, a two-storey house, which is relatively light in construction terms, will only need simple, 600 mm wide foundations. If you are unlucky, and the subsoil is poor, you may have to keep digging until good ground is reached, or use special foundations such as piles.

Table 10: Minimum Width of Strip Foundations			Total load of load-bearing walling not more than (kN/linear meter)					
			20	30	40	50	60	70
Type of subsoil	Condition of subsoil	Field test applicable	Minimum width of strip foundation (mm)					
i Rock	not inferior to sandstone, limestone or firm chalk	requires at least a pneumatic, or other mechanically operated, pick for excavation	In each case equal to the width of wall					
ii gravel sand	compact compact	requires pick for excavation. Wooden peg 500mm square in cross-section hard to drive beyond 150mm	250	300	400	500	600	650
iii clay sandy clay	stiff stiff	cannot be moulded with the fingers and requires a pick and pneumatic, or other mechanically operated, spade for its removal	250	300	400	500	600	650
iv clay sandy clay	firm firm	can be moulded by substantial pressure with the fingers and can be excavated with graft or spade	300	350	450	600	750	850
v sand silty sand clayey sand	loose loose loose	can be excavated with a spade. Wooden peg 50mm square in cross-section can be easily driven	400	600				
vi silt clay sandy clay silty clay	soft soft soft soft	fairly easily moulded in the fingers and readily excavated	450	650				
vii silt clay sandy clay silty clay	very soft very soft very soft very soft	natural sample in winter conditions exudes between fingers when squeezed in fist	600	850				

Note: In relation to types v, vi and vii, foundations do not fall within the provisions of this section if the total load exceeds 30kN/m.

From The Building Regulations 2000: Approved Document A, ODPM © Crown Copyright 2004

Trial Holes

Trial holes are an immensely useful way of learning more about a site, and are essential if there is any doubt about what lies beneath the plot. They are best dug before any formal contract is signed, and certainly before detailed construction drawings are prepared. Ideally, several should be excavated, to a depth of at least 3 m, at points just beyond where you expect to build – to avoid compromising the bearing ability of the ground for foundations. It is not a 'DIY job' – apart from being hard work, it could also be dangerous, and you need to hire a local groundworker with a digger. The subsoil exposed by the trial hole should be inspected by the engineer, architect and building control officer. The latter usually has the final say over the foundation depth and construction, so it is all to the good if you have an idea of what will be expected at an early stage in the project.

Adjacent Buildings

A close examination of buildings next to, or close by, the plot may give an early warning of problems below ground. If the area is susceptible to subsidence caused by mining, or a sudden change in the subsoil, there will almost certainly be tell-tale signs on existing buildings, in the form of cracks to the walls. However, the diagnosis of the cause of this cracking is an expert job, so be careful not to jump to any hasty conclusions.

Clay

Clay subsoil is not ideal to build on. This is because when it gets wet, it expands, and when it dries, it shrinks. These movements are not great, but the forces involved are considerable. The top layer of clay tends to be wetter in winter than in summer, causing seasonal shifts in the first metre or so of the subsoil. The effect of this on footings that have been set within this movement zone is that the walls will crack. These cracks open out further in the summer and reduce again in winter, but the long-term effect is progressive damage to the property. In the mid-1970s, the UK experienced an unusually severe drought. The widescale damage to buildings in clay areas that resulted led to the Building Regulations being revised to ensure that all new foundations were set low enough to avoid future problems. In practice this means that in a clay area, the foundations have to be at least 1 m deep rather than the minimum for good ground, which is about 600 mm.

Clay and Trees

If there are trees on a site in a clay area, there is a further complication. Trees draw moisture from the ground, especially in summer. Their roots penetrate deep into the earth, and accentuate the seasonal wetting and drying of the ground, which in turn magnifies its expansion and contraction. This effect even continues for several seasons after the tree has been felled. So when you are inspecting a site with clay subsoil, look for trees near to where the building is likely to be – but also tree stumps, or depressions in the ground that suggest a tree has been removed. The extra depth needed to compensate for the effect of tree roots varies according to the type of tree (some soak up more water than others) and the nature of the clay, which can vary from 'high shrinkability' to 'low shrinkability'. The very worst case would require a 3.5 m depth, which is more cost-effective if mini-piles are used rather than conventional strip or trench-fill foundations.

This trial excavation has revealed a drain, power cable and a concealed sump, as well as the condition of the subsoil.

Look for cracks in existing buildings.

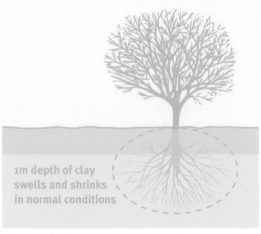

1m depth of clay swells and shrinks in normal conditions

The zone of influence of trees extends deep into the soil.

Mining Subsidence

As a mineral seam, such as coal, is mined underground using modern methods, the shaft is allowed to collapse as the mining machinery progresses. High above, on the surface, the ground level drops a few centimetres. As the mine progresses below a house, the ground level
drops in a wave that moves across the site, until the building eventually settles. Any damage that results is then made good at the mining company's expense. Current or future mining activity should be picked up by the planning authority and your solicitor's search. If a seam is worked out, it should not present a problem. Another risk to be aware of in mining areas are old, unrecorded seams which are only partially collapsed. Some of these, such as bell pits, go back to prehistoric times. If their presence is suspected, the building control officer may require deep boreholes to be dug. Where 'open cast' mining has occurred – i.e. the topsoil has been scraped off, the seam beneath mined, and the hole has then been backfilled – existing trial holes or records should be available.

Filled Ground

To avoid damaging settlement occurring, foundations should be built directly on to 'virgin', or undisturbed, ground. This is because, once subsoil has been excavated it cannot, in normal circumstances, be sufficiently compacted to avoid it settling under the weight of the new building. If a site has been excavated and then backfilled, any new foundations will have to be taken down to the level of the undisturbed ground. This may require special foundations, adding many thousands of pounds to the build cost.

Contaminated Land

This is another kind of pollution, although much harder to spot than the above-ground type.
This is more of a risk on a 'brownfield' site, where the land has been previously built on, or if it has been used before for an industrial purpose. Contamination means that the land must present significant harm to people or the environment. The local authority keeps a register of contaminated land, and has the power to enforce its cleaning up. Usually the polluter pays, but, if the latter cannot be found, the burden falls on the current owner. Sometimes the land is left, since it is safer to leave it undisturbed. Solicitors' searches often reveal the risk of contamination, or an honest vendor may reveal it to purchasers. All suspicions should be investigated, since decontamination costs are usually high.

Demolished Buildings

If a building is to be demolished to make way for the new house, this is not necessarily a problem – apart from the demolition cost. Provided that there are no cellars, the new foundations can cut through the existing ones, and a suspended floor slab can be used to bridge over the fill and rubble that is left below ground.

Sulphates

These chemicals are present in the ground in some areas, and attack mortar, blockwork and foundations – anything made from concrete. If there is a risk of sulphates in the soil or groundwater, the building control officer will usually know, and a test can be carried out. This problem is dealt with by introducing an additive to any mortar or concrete used, and by avoiding the use of susceptible concrete blocks below ground.

Services

'Services' means facilities that are supplied or provided to a property by others, for the use or convenience of the occupiers: power, communications, sewers, etc. Some sites are sold as 'serviced' plots, but the vendor or agents should be asked to elaborate on this description if details are not volunteered. Any new service connections necessary can add thousands of pounds to the development costs of a site.

It is possible to occupy and live on a site without services being provided by the outside world – several experimental houses have been constructed in the UK that do this. However, with the technology currently available, it is expensive and inconvenient. Alternatives to all mains services are available – even toilets that hygienically recycle human waste products for the garden, eliminating the need for a foul sewer. Some of these alternatives may devalue a house, but in many rural areas substitutes are seen as a part of everyday life.

Make a point of studying the ground and street around the site, looking for any manhole covers or service-access points, which will indicate services in proximity to the site.

Statutory Authorities

As part of your desk search (see 'Finding a Site' section, earlier), the statutory authorities should be contacted. For a small fee, they should be able to provide Ordnance Survey plans of the area around the site. Unfortunately, these plans are described in technical terms by the authorities as 'approximate', and they accept no liability for their accuracy, i.e. they could easily be wrong. Any records should always be backed up by site observations and investigations. However, you should at least be able to check whether there are any major services which are, supplying other properties or running across the plot. If there are any, it will be quite hard to build near them, and almost impossible to build directly over them. They will

Getting services connected often means a long wait.

also be expensive to divert, so, if the vendor has not declared them when offering the plot for sale, the consequent cost of dealing with them can legitimately be deducted from the sale price.

At the same time as finding out where the services are running, the connection costs should also be identified and plugged into your budget calculation. This can easily run into many thousands of pounds, depending on the services concerned and their proximity to the site. If you have to go across someone else's land to connect, you must get their approval, and they may charge you for the privilege.

Service providers are notoriously slow to respond to requests for information. Inquiries have to be in writing, and should be sent out as soon as you are seriously interested in a site.

Mains Drainage

One of the first things to do when inspecting a site is to look for manholes, and if you find any, lift them and look down the drain. If there are no manholes on the site, look in the adjacent road (they are quite widely spaced, so you will need to take a walk in both directions). Modern drainage systems are split into surface water (rainwater) and foul (from toilets, sinks, etc.). So, if you find two manholes next to each other, apparently marking parallel runs, this is a good sign.

A single drain indicates that the public sewer may be combined, i.e. the same pipe takes foul and surface water. Combined drains are no longer built by service providers, and are considered a bad thing generally since surface-water drainage arrives in much greater volume than foul, but, because it is then mixed, it all has to be treated as foul, placing an unnecessary demand on sewage works. Consequently, if a development site has to rely on a combined drain, the water authority is likely to refuse permission to connect surface water drainage to it.

If a main drain is closer than 30 m to the site, and it is possible to reach it without crossing someone else's land, the Building Regulations give the local authority the power to compel you to connect to it.

Another possibility is that mains drainage is available, but it is too shallow to reach from the new house while maintaining the correct fall for the drains. In this case, a pump is necessary, at a possible cost of £3,000–£4,000, along with a maintenance liability which will probably last the lifetime of the property.

Soakaways and Septic Tanks

If there is no mains drainage to the site, and none in striking distance, you will have to use other methods to deal with the drainage requirement of the new house. One way of doing this, and a strategy that is increasing in popularity, is 'rainwater harvesting': collecting the rainwater and reusing it – either for the garden or for flushing toilets – or even chemically treating it and drinking it. This helps reduce the need for water-treatment plants and reduces water bills at the same time. More conventionally, the surface water can be run to a soakaway – a large hole in the ground filled with rubble, where the water collects and seeps into the ground, or a network of pipes with holes in them that does the same job. Soakaways should be no nearer than 5 m to the house, and if the ground is poorly drained (e.g. heavy clay), a large area will be needed to disperse the water. If the site is not big enough to achieve this, it may not be possible to develop the site at all – unless a watercourse can be drained into, or you can reach a deal with a neighbour to use their main drain connection.

Foul drainage is slightly trickier to handle on site. The old-fashioned method of a cesspool is still used today in extreme circumstances, but there is no doubt that this devalues a property. The best alternative, assuming you do not want to recycle and put last year's waste products on the roses via a composting toilet, is a septic tank. This consists of a bulb-shaped plastic chamber, buried in the ground, where the foul waste is collected. Nature, in the form of anaerobic bacteria, then goes to

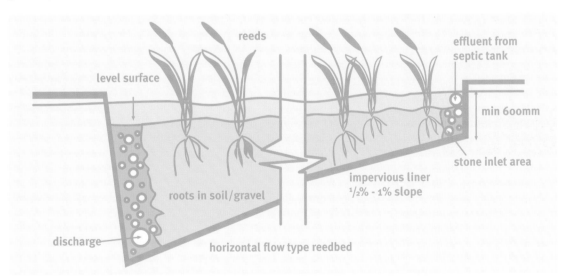

You can direct the outfall of a septic tank into a reed-bed and pond.

work, and eventually relatively harmless run-off overflows into the ground via a network of pipes. Building control require a septic tank to be 12 m away from the house, and usually ask for proof that the ground drainage is suitable to disperse the outfall. The latter is achieved by digging a hole to a set size, filling it with water and waiting to see how long it takes to drain away; a test described in the Building Regulations. If it doesn't drain away, then a septic tank is not going to be viable. Once in use, it will need emptying once a year. A more adventurous solution is to run the outfall from the soakaway to a reed-bed and a small pond.

If the ground is poorly drained and if either a pond or a watercourse is available, a treatment plant may be used to discharge into them. These speed up the effect of the friendly bacteria, by stirring up the mixture, and the resulting outfall is said by the manufacturers to be sterile. There is a high initial outlay for installing a treatment plant (£4,000–£5,000), and an ongoing cost to run and maintain it. Any discharge to or near a watercourse will need approval from the Environment Agency.

Water

Unless you are lucky enough to be able to sink your own borehole, or brave enough to recycle rainwater, a mains water supply is essential. If there are other houses close to your site, it is a reasonable assumption that this is available. However, many modern appliances require an appreciable pressure to work, and an adequate supply-pipe diameter, and both these should checked. For example, a pressured system for hot water requires both of these.

Electricity

A mains supply is essential for most people, and the local supplier can quote a cost for providing it if it is not already available on site. Its presence on a site is potentially a serious hazard if the exact location of buried cables is not known, because excavations may lead to builders unexpectedly coming in contact with them. Above ground, cables supplying directly to buildings are still to be found – especially in rural areas. There are minimum distances to electricity mains, closer than which a building cannot go, and special precautions are necessary during construction. If a cable is in the way of building works, it is possible to have it diverted, usually at significant cost.

Just because there are services available to other houses, don't assume that it is acceptable to add more load on to the existing system, especially in rural areas. If an underground electricity cable has to be upgraded it can cost thousands.

Gas

Although inconvenient, a lack of mains gas is not unusual in villages, and would not devalue a property provided the other houses in the area were also without it. Electricity can be used for cooking, but is not particularly cost-effective as a source of heating. There are three ways of storing gas delivered to a site by lorry – in an above-ground tank, a below-ground tank, and a cylinder. There are rules regarding how close tanks can be, both to the house and the boundary (as much as 7.5 m away for a large tank), and limits to the length of hose that comes from the tanker that refills it. Consequently, when examining a site where you expect to rely on a gas tank, you should establish if the plot is large enough to fit one in.

Oil

Oil is similar to gas, with respect to its position on the site. Oil prices are quite volatile, so it varies in cost-effectiveness to gas, depending on the international market.

Legal Issues

Solicitors

Solicitors are essential in the process of checking for problems and risks before 'signing on the dotted line'. However, a solicitor who carries out ordinary conveyancing work may not necessarily have much experience with land purchases – they rarely visit the site itself, for example. So you should back up the usual legal investigations with your own checks, and have a basic understanding of the main pitfalls.

Ownership and Boundaries

One of the simplest issues, you would think, but it has been known to generate huge problems. Even with the land around occupied houses, boundary disputes are one of the more common causes of disagreements between neighbours. The older maps found with deeds and conveyancing documents are rarely precise, or to an accurate scale. Land that has been bought or sold is now recorded at the Land Registry, which was founded in 1926 to reduce disputes regarding ownership. But some land is still not registered, and, if it is, the maps used are usually 1:1,250-scale Ordnance Survey sheets, which do not show much detail. One of the many benefits of commissioning an accurate

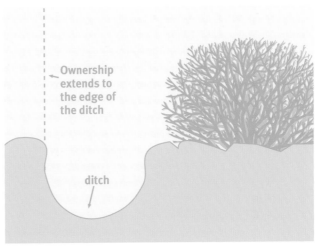

Sometimes the boundary by a ditch is not where you think it should be.

measured survey (see 'Site Surveys' section, earlier) is that you can 'walk the site' with it, and the boundaries can be unequivocally identified and agreed with the vendor.

Sometimes, a boundary may not be where it appears to be on the map: for example, traditionally, if a boundary is formed by a hedge and a ditch, both belong to the land on the hedge side.

Ransom Strips

A classic scenario, known to frustrate even the sharpest of developers, is where access to a site is across a thin strip of land owned by someone else. This is called a ransom strip, simply because its owner can demand a large payment to co-operate and make the site viable. Sometimes this doesn't even show up on the Land Registry records – and it may even be land beyond the site, where visibility is required to satisfy the highway officer.

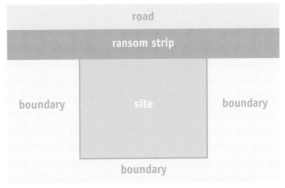

A ransom strip can prevent a site from being developed.

Covenants, Easements and Wayleaves

Even if someone owns some land, they don't necessarily have total control over it. All the above examples involve other people or organisations having rights over a site, and most should be shown up by the solicitor's search. They may be exercised by other landowners: for example, covenants exist that give a right of approval to any building works or changes in land use. Or they may be imposed by services suppliers, a classic example of which are the easements which give power companies the right to access mains electricity cables across a site, and to prevent building work within 3 m of a buried cable. Sometimes they can be negotiated away, bought off, or, if it seems that there is no-one around to enforce them, insured against. Rights that have been accumulated over time may not be recorded anywhere, but, provided they can be proved, they may be legal. All this underlines the importance of a proper walk over the site – looking for clues, such as unexpected gates to adjoining land – and of little chats with the neighbours.

Footpaths

Footpaths can be a legal nightmare. They cannot be easily removed, and even diverting them is a major exercise that may take years. Their exact routes may not be recorded, but it is usually the shortest way between the points of entry. It may be possible to accommodate a footpath which runs along or near to a boundary, or screen the house and gardens from the view of passing walkers.

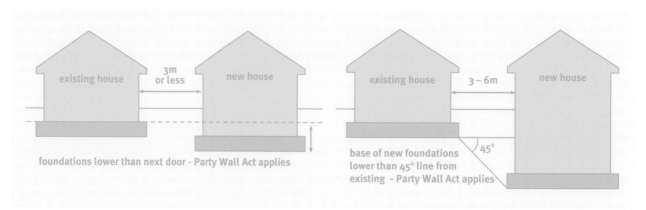

The Party Wall etc Act will apply in these situations.

Party Walls

The Party Wall etc Act 1996 was designed to help resolve disputes between neighbours over maintenance of walls and fences along, or close to, the boundary between two properties. It works best in tight urban situations, where there are many parties jostling up against each other. In rural or suburban situations it can seem like an unnecessary aggravation. The main concern for one-off houses is that the legislation may require that a notice is served on a neighbour if any work is to be carried out within 6 m of their house. There are certain things, to do with the design of the foundations, which affect whether or not the Act will apply, and professional advice is essential if you suspect that it may pertain.

Adverse Possession

If someone occupies a piece of land without the owner of that land objecting, or charging rent, they can lay claim to it by application to the Land Registry. This is called adverse possession. It means that the ownership boundary indicated on the legal documents must be carefully checked on site. It used to be easier for people to acquire land in this way, but since October 2003 the rules have been tightened up, so that the registered owner of the land should have been informed by the Land Registry if someone has attempted to claim part of the site.

Locality and History

Unless you have found a site in the middle of the countryside, or on an uninhabited island, the surrounding community and how you interact with it will have a profound affect on your enjoyment of your new home. There is a lot to be gained from a bit of research at the local library, or some apparently casual chats with neighbours, local builders and the drinkers at the local pub. It may be hard to find the time to do this along with all the more formal things that need to be sorted out, especially if you are not living locally, but any developer will tell you that this is one of the most essential parts of a site investigation.

One word of caution. If the site in question is not widely known to be available, a bit of subterfuge and secrecy are necessary. In this situation, you cannot trust anyone you do not know to be reliable – not even the professionals, a few of whom will take commissions for finding land on behalf of builders and developers, and who may leak news of the site. When you employ solicitors, architects or others in the early stages, do not reveal the location until it is necessary and make it clear in writing that you expect the details to be kept strictly confidential – at least you will then have some recourse, by claiming breach of contract or professional standards if you lose the site by their default.

History

There are often booklets available at the local library which give the history of an area. This may seem of academic interest, until you find out it gives the locations of disused graveyards, and a description of previous land uses in the area. For example, a reference to tanning works or a blacksmith's indicates possible contaminated land.

Architectural Character

An understanding of the traditional local building styles, or 'vernacular', is a useful asset – particularly in Conservation Areas, or near listed buildings. If the close proximity of many older buildings to the site suggests that the planners and local 'movers and shakers' are going to expect you to blend in with it, you need to be sure that you can accommodate your requirements within the likely style. For example, in many rural areas, the predominant style is the 'room-in-the-roof' cottage. This will mean that the ground floor will be 50–60 per cent bigger than the first floor – which is fine if you do not need a lot of bedrooms or don't mind sleeping on the ground floor, but not so good for a large family. Just because a building is a different style to the surrounding architecture, it does not mean that it is in some way detrimental to the area. Often a well-designed modern building can complement the character of its surroundings.

A building does not have to match in with the existing architecture to enhance a street.

Privacy

Stand in the middle of your site and take a 360° look around. How many windows can you see? If you can see a window to someone else's bedroom, landing or living room, there is a good chance that they can see you. If a site has a lot of overlooking windows, it might be impossible to have complete privacy in the garden, or even in many of the rooms in the house itself. Planning departments used to enforce rules about how close main windows to houses could be, but the pressure to find more land for housing, and increasing densities, mean that these are sometimes relaxed, particularly in urban areas. High fences are also frowned on by the planners, and high screens of trees will soon be controlled as well, so it is not easy to shut people out in such circumstances.

Road Names

Traditionally, road names reflect their location, which may give some clues to previous uses or ownership. Some real examples: 'Watery Lane' suggests a high water table; 'Glebe Street' indicates that the land has been owned by the church, giving a lead as to where to find more information; 'Barker Gate' comes from the use of bark in the leather tanning process, suggesting possible contaminated land; 'Graveyard Lane' is self-explanatory.

Nearby Features

Proximity to desirable features could have a big impact on your quality of life once in occupation. No parents need to be told the importance of a good school nearby, but if you are too close, or on one of the main routes for secondary school pupils, will this result in nuisance? It depends on your point of view, but you should be aware of the implications before you buy. Good public transport links will not necessarily be a priority when you move in, but, after building their own property, many people stay into retirement, when a local bus may prove a vital link. Innovative public transport may increase the value of property over time. For example, in Nottingham some properties close to the new tram links have recently gone up in value, as they are seen as an asset because they make commuting easier and quicker.

Neighbours

The importance of talking to the neighbours at an early stage cannot be overstated. They may well resent a new development on open land next door, but if they are subjected to a charm offensive, they may realise that the alternative to you may be far less palatable – for example, a developer who will move in, maximise the site's profit-making capability, and selling it on without giving their concerns a second thought. Neighbours will probably know the history of a site, and might tell you things the vendor may not have mentioned. If they turn out to be unhelpful, miserable, or hostile, you may decide that you don't want them as neighbours anyway, and withdraw from the purchase. Alternatively, you may be able to negotiate something that the vendor has not been able to – like access to their manholes, saving the cost of a main drainage connection.

Security

A site that backs on to common land or a park, has a nearby footpath, is in an isolated location, has poor street lighting, or is near a deprived area, will present security risks that must be addressed in the design, but will also need dealing with at the construction stage. Something must be included in the budget to allow for this. In extreme cases, builders will factor in the cost of an overnight security guard to their build cost.

Valuations

Maximum Development Potential

When a professional developer buys a site and builds on it, their main concern is to get the best return for their investment, regardless of the nature of the development. They calculate the optimum size and quality of a house on a given site, based on the average selling price of similar houses in the area. If they build a house that is too small for a site, they will under-develop it. They will not get the best return for the investment, and may even lose money on the deal. Conversely, if they build a large, detached five-bedroom house in an area where all the other houses are three-bedroom semis, they are unlikely to achieve a high enough sale price to generate a profit. If you are building your own house, the same rules apply. Many people choose not to worry too much about the resale, because they don't intend to move again for a long time. However, all developers, even amateur ones, should make the calculation, and know how much it will cost them to break the rules.

Estate Agents and Valuers

If a bank or building society is involved, they will insist on a proper estimate of the likely value of the completed house before agreeing to fund the development. Even if there is no lender involved, it is still essential to get a valuation. It is possible to collect quite a lot of information about the general area from estate agency and government websites, but there is no substitute for an experienced local estate agent to do this job. It is one of the most vital pieces of information needed to assess the financial viability of the project.

Summary

- Don't be pressured into a hasty decision unless you can afford the risk.
- Get full details from the estate agent or vendor.
- Make your own initial visit and check:

  Dimensions, Boundaries, Ownership, Locality.
- If the site passes the first visit, use the detailed Site Assessment Checklist for a detailed investigation.
- You will not be able to check everything – balance likelihood against consequences.
- Ask 'Why has it not been built on before?'; use your imagination: the site might have been made unattractive by its current use (or disuse).
- Speak to the vendors and neighbours, but don't rely on anecdotal reports alone.
- Be prepared to spend some money to get important information.
- Professionals who can help:

  Architect, Site Surveyor, Planning Officer, Building Control Office, Solicitor.

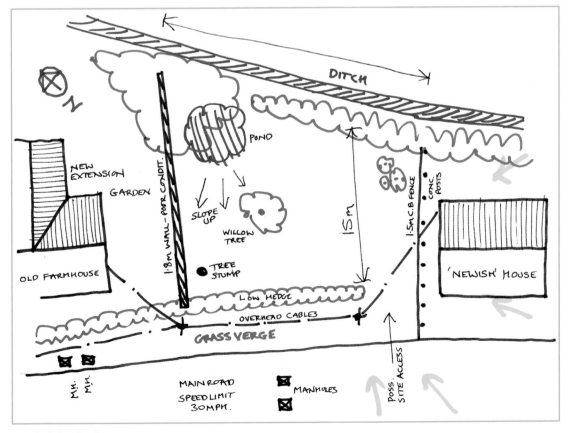

A typical site sketch

Site Assessment Checklist

The following list of questions can be used as a basis for anticipating any problems that may arise once the design and construction process has started. It is not exhaustive, since every site is unique. However, most of the common issues are covered. Most of the items listed will simply be crossed out as not relevant, but many will require further investigation by yourselves or your professional advisors.

Site Surveys
A typical site survey should include:

- North point
- Existing boundaries, and type
  e.g. fence, ditch, hedge, etc.
- Levels in and around the site, to a fixed datum
- Existing buildings adjacent to the site

- Adjacent roads, pavements and footpaths
- Trees and significant vegetation
- Manholes
- Any features e.g. rock outcrop, pits, ponds, spoil heaps, etc.

Questions to Ask About the Planning Permission
General
- Is the planning approval Outline or Detailed?

- How easily was it obtained?

- When does the planning permission expire?

- Do you have copies of whole approval document?

- What conditions are there on the approval?

- Will your design get approval if it's different?

- Do you have a copy of OS plan indicating the land that has the approval?

- Local Plan checked – any future development/roads, etc. planned in the area?

- What are planning officer's comments about the site?

- Will you overlook neighbours' windows or garden?

- Is there a building line?

- Are there any Tree Preservation Orders in place, or likely to be in the future?

Context
- Is the prevailing character of the new and traditional local buildings valued by the planners?

- What styles of development have been recently approved nearby the site?

- Is the site in or near an area of special control?
  - ◯ Greenbelt
  - ◯ National Park
  - ◯ Listed Building
  - ◯ Area of archaeological interest
  - ◯ Area of Outstanding Natural Beauty
  - ◯ Site of Special Scientific Interest
  - ◯ Conservation Area
  - ◯ Ancient Monuments

Site Assessment Checklist - continued

Highways Issues
- Are visibility splays required and can they be achieved within the site?

- What is the requirement for car parking within the site?

- Can a car leave the site in forward gear, and is there room to turn round within the site?

English Nature or local equivalent
- Are there likely to be any of the following on, or close to, the site:

  ◯ Bats   ◯ Owls   ◯ Badgers   ◯ Newts   ◯ Rare plants (e.g. orchids)

What to Look for on Site

Climate and Site Features
- What direction is the sun relative to the site?

- Is the site exposed to wind and driving rain on any side?

- What trees are on the site? Are they a benefit, or a problem?

- Is there a change in level across the site?

- Are there any sources of noise in the area?

- Are there/have there been any sources of pollution in the area?

- Is Japanese Knotweed present on site?

Ground Conditions
- Trial hole results (subsoil type)?

- Local geological map available?

- Building control officer's comments?

- Any sign of subsidence to existing buildings?

- Is there any mining in the area?

- Any risk of tree roots damaging the foundations?

- Are trees and shrinkable clay both present on the site?

- Is there a high water table, risking flooding or impeding foundation construction?

Site Assessment Checklist - continued

- Is there any risk of landslip?

- Is the ground undisturbed, i.e. not backfilled?

- Is there any ground contamination?

- Is there any evidence of demolished buildings?

- Are sulphate levels in the soil significant?

- Is the area at risk from radon gas?

- Is the site close to the coast, with a risk of erosion?

- Has the site been used previously, has this caused any pollution of the soil?

Services

- Is mains foul drainage available on the site?

- If no to the above, is the site drainage adequate for a septic tank, and are there any water courses nearby?

- Is mains water available on the site?

- Is mains electricity available?

- Is mains gas available? If no, is the site big enough for safe fuel storage?

- Where are service runs located? Are there any, above or below ground, across the site?

Legal Issues

- Do the boundaries on the plan from the deeds match the site?

- Has solicitor's search highlighted any problems?

- Does the vendor really own the whole site?

- Are there any covenants, easements or wayleaves? If yes, are they redundant?

- Are there any footpaths across, or near to, the site?

- Are there any neighbouring house walls, or other walls and fences, on the boundary?

Site Assessment Checklist - continued

Locality & History

- Can you locate any historical maps of the immediate area?

- Will you match in or contrast with the dominant architectural character?

- What are the views out of the site on each side?

- What is the land immediately around the site used for?

- Is the site overlooked by other houses or roadways on any side?

- What has the site been used for in the past?

- Are there any road or area names that give clues to past uses?

- What is the prevailing socio-economic group in the area and are you happy with it?

- What are nearby facilities like? E.g. schools, public transport, shops, etc?

- Is there a local history society? If yes, who runs it and can you meet them?

- What are the neighbours like, and do they welcome the development?

- Can the site be made secure, during and after the build?

- Can the site be easily reached by delivery vehicles, especially during construction?

Valuations

- What are the ceiling-prices for different sorts of house in the area?

- What will be the sale value of the finished development?

- What is left if you subtract the land value from the value of the completed house?

- Is the resulting figure, above, enough to build your home?

- What is the maximum development potential of the site, and how will your house compare?

Buying a Plot

Once you have found a site that satisfies your requirements and is a good place to build your home, you must buy it as soon as possible. For all but the most fortunate site hunters, speed is now of the essence. You cannot afford the luxury of contemplation, or to wait in the hope that the price will come down. If you are right about the plot, then there will plenty of other buyers about to put in an offer, and others hot on the trail who will soon find out about it. Your careful planning should have ensured that you have already found your finance provider, and it will not take you long to sort out a mortgage offer.

Who Owns the Land?

Before you make an offer on a plot, if it has not been formally presented to the market by an agent, you may not be sure who actually owns some or all of the land. Finding the owner, in order to make an offer can sometimes be a problem. Apart from knocking on all the neighbours' doors, the other, more formal, source of information in England and Wales is the Land Registry (the regional equivalents are the Registers of Scotland Executive Agency, and Land Registers of Northern Ireland). In each case, this is the public body that is building a database of land ownership. Provided that you know the exact postal address, and are prepared to pay a small fee, you can find out who owns a plot. That is, provided that it is on the register – registration did not become compulsory until 1990.

Valuing the Plot

Up to this point you have probably been using the 'land cost to be one-third to a half of project cost' calculation as a rule of thumb, but now that you have to bid for a real plot you need to work out more accurately whether you can afford it, and get an idea of what it might be worth to others.

The Land Registry, Registers of Scotland Executive Agency, or LRNI also hold data on property prices. On their websites, they will provide average prices for types of house for any given postcode, which is useful information when you are trying to decide how to pitch your bid. You can engage a local estate agent or land valuer to come up with a valuation. But there are several problems with this. The first is that estate agents often have no real idea how much a plot is worth. They rely on monitoring how much similar properties sell for to estimate the value – which is fine with whole houses, many of which are sold every week. But plots are extremely rare by comparison, and there is unlikely to be enough data for agents to look back at. This is one reason that estate agents prefer to sell land at auction.

Whilst you are looking for a plot, you will accumulate a lot of information on land prices in the area in which you are searching. As a result, you yourself may be in a position to estimate figures that are more accurate predictions than most agents, especially the ones who only see a few plots a year.

There are ways of calculating what land is worth to commercially minded developers, because they all tend to use similar methods. However, you need to know what the land is worth to you, given that your project will be individual. You will not necessarily build a house calculated to get the best market value out of the site. You might build a smaller or bigger house than would fit this description. Also, you will have your own idea as to how much profit you wish to make. You may have been looking for so long that you don't care if you lose money – in which case you will value the site at a higher price than most others.

The calculations below have been simplified, but the general principles hold good. The reasons for the differences are that people who are building for themselves tend to spend more money on features of the house that don't necessarily enhance the value of the plot, and quite often build to higher prices than developers. Those who have been hunting for a good plot for many years, and do

How to Calculate the Value of the Plot to the Commercial Property Market		
Value of the best house the site could take when complete	=	£200,000
Subtract the cost of building the house, including overheads	-	£120,000
Subtract a profit margin	-	£30,000
Remainder is how much the plot is worth	=	£50,000

How to Calculate the Value of the Plot to You		
Value of the house you would like to build	=	£195,000
Subtract the cost of building the house, renting, etc.	-	£130,000
Subtract any profit that you would like to make	-	£5,000
Remainder is how much the plot is worth to you	=	£60,000

not expect to move for a long time after they have built, will actually add in a figure as a loss in place of allowing for a profit, simply to be sure of getting it. There is nothing wrong with this, as long as they have made the calculation and know what they are doing.

Of course, these calculations do not reflect the fact that the land is bought at one time, and the completed property valued much later, after the increase in house prices has had an effect. This partly explains the misleading figures sometimes quoted, which suggest that it is easy for amateur developers to make a big profit. It isn't, but it can be done. However, few people ever redo their budget calculation at the end of the project and factor in things like finance costs and house-price inflation.

Methods of Selling Land

When a plot is brought to market, the agents advising the vendor should decide how to get the best possible price. To do this they will pick from a selection of sales strategies, sometimes using a combination of them as they start to sense how keen the market is.

Inviting Offers

Just like buying a house, potential purchasers may be invited to make offers, and once an offer is received that is acceptable to the vendor, the sale is agreed. The disadvantage of this is that an accurate sale price has to be fixed, something that the agents may not be able to do. If the vendor has slightly unrealistic expectations as a result, the sale process may take much longer.

When you make an offer for a plot to the agents by telephone, always back it up with a fax sent straight afterwards. A fax is a timed and dated record of your offer, and doing this will ensure that it is referred to the vendor accurately and quickly.

Informal Tenders

If the last method ends up becoming protracted, and negotiations have opened up with several prospective purchasers, the agents may decide to ask for tenders from all of them, by a certain date. Once the tender date has been reached, the bids are opened and the vendor can then pick the highest. However, the vendor is not bound to accept, and the result may be further negotiations with one or two of the preferred bidders.

When submitting a tender, take a leaf from the builders' book and never bid a round figure, e.g. bid £101,000 in the hope that the next highest is £100,000.

Auctions

If the agents decide to put the plot up for auction, and you wish to make a bid, be prepared for a nerve-racking experience. An auction immediately hands the advantage over to developers and builders, who are speculating business capital rather than their life savings, and they are more used to the process. Also, because once you have made the highest bid, you are the owner, all your site investigation – and the legal issues surrounding it – will have had to be done to a sufficient level for you to be confident that you are bidding the right price. To do this properly will take time and money, which could be to no avail if you discover that the site was more expensive than you calculated. If you do the minimum, to save architect's and legal costs, you dramatically increase the risk of buying a site with a hidden problem.

Agents often significantly understate the value of land going to auction. This is because it guarantees a good turnout on the day, which is supposed to drive bids higher but also makes the event appear more successful than if a realistic price has been suggested.

Even if a plot is announced as going to auction, it may still be worth putting in a bid beforehand. It is not unheard of for a vendor to decide to accept an early bid, rather than wait for the auction. Likewise, after an auction is over it is worth ringing the agent to check that that the land has been sold, because if it has not reached its reserve price, it will still be available.

Talking Up the Price

Once you are involved in the negotiations for a plot, the agents may try various tactics to get you to speed up the process, or increase you offer. Sometimes they will refer to another party, just as keen as you, who is bidding more, and ask if you would like to increase your offer. At other times they will suggest that whoever is ready to exchange first will get the land. You will have to make a judgement as to how genuine these other bidders are, and whether or not they are being told the same things about you. Try to establish contact with the vendor if at all possible. They may choose not to follow the hard-headed advice of their agent, particularly if they live next to the plot, and you may be their new neighbours.

But you must be strong enough to walk away if you start to feel overly pressured, or that games are being played – you will find other plots in the future, and probably better deals, and, if you call the vendor's bluff, you might just get this one on terms that are acceptable to you.

Options

There are ways around much of the stress and tension generated by buying a plot, if you can get the vendor to agree. A trick much used by developers is to take out an option on the site. This means that you enter into a legal agreement, at a cost to you, that the owner of the land will not sell it to anyone else for a fixed period, giving you the option of acquiring it if you decide to. If, at the end of this period, you have still not bought it, the owner can sell it or keep it – or you could negotiate a further option. This is of most use where a site does not have planning approval, and the odds of it being granted are relatively low. For example, if there is a rumour that a new road is going to be built, developers may take out ten-year options on the land in the area it would be built, in the hope that within this time the road will be built and planning restrictions will be changed. These are all long shots, but if you do it in a lot of different situations, the odds are that at least one or two of them will come off, and a very large profit will be made to compensate for all the failures.

Options are not ideal as a method of acquiring a one-off plot for your own house, unless you have the time and money. The vendor will probably not agree to a long wait, unless the chances of getting planning approval are very slim, because there is a bigger profit in getting permission themselves and then putting it on the open market.

Conditional Contracts

What may be more attractive than options to the owner of a plot is a conditional contract. This ties the potential purchaser into buying, provided a stated condition is fulfilled, such as the granting of planning approval or an adjacent tranche of land being acquired. This arrangement gives both parties some comfort, because the vendor knows that the purchaser is obliged to buy, and the purchaser knows that the land will not be sold to someone else after time and money has been laid out to get the condition fulfilled.

Scotland

The legal process of purchasing land and other property is quite different in Scotland than in the rest of the UK, in that you are expected to be bound to an offer as soon as it is accepted, The offer is usually made by sealed bids to be received by a given date, and the sale is then concluded very quickly. As with an auction, all the preliminary work should be done beforehand, which increases the risk of wasted time and money.

Finding a Designer

At this point you have worked out your budget, got a clear idea of your requirements, arranged finance and had your offer on a site accepted. It is finally time to get some drawings prepared. Picking the right professional is obviously essential. But to avoid a long, drawn-out design process, you have to be very clear about what you need from the new house, have agreed it with all the family and then have explained this to your architect. The architect in turn must be able to put across ideas and put forward suggestions in a clear way. As with any creative project, good communication between client and designer is vital.

The Design Process

This begins earlier than you may think. You will have to make choices that directly affect the design of your house in the very early days, when you first contemplate the project. As you gather more information about where the house is to be built, and what your expectations are for it, the design is already beginning to develop.

However at this stage, a landmark is reached – the engaging of someone to turn your hopes and dreams into a real building. All the available information you have gathered has to be recorded, collated, and presented to the designer. At the same time, the architect should also embark on an information gathering process before starting to explore possible design solutions. But, first of all, you have to find that key person.

Architects do not just deal with the design of houses. They can also work out how it is built, manage the contract and generally act as your guide throughout the whole process.

Working With a Designer

There are several types of designer who may be able to help you. The custom for people outside the construction industry is to refer to all of them by the generic term 'architect'. As shown below, there are in fact a number of different kinds of professionals who design houses, all with different types and levels of skill. In the interests of brevity, generalisations are made here in describing them. The experience of many clients has shown that these categories are useful as an initial guide, but that there are many others factors apart from paper qualifications that will decide who is right for your project.

Architects

The title 'Architect' is protected by law and only designers who have completed a tough seven-year training course are allowed to use it. People who style themselves as 'architectural consultants' and 'architectural designers' are not architects, and do not necessarily have any formal qualifications at all. An architect's training is rigorous, and all aspects of the design and construction process are learnt, from smaller to larger-scale buildings.

The RIBA logo can only be used by its members.

All professionals who practice as architects must be registered with the Architects Registration Board (ARB), a government organisation that is responsible for dealing with complaints as well as keeping the register. Uniquely in the construction industry, this regulatory body has a majority of people from outside the profession on its governing council. Most architects are also members of the Royal Institute of British Architects (RIBA), although this is not obligatory. Architects are known for their ability to design, but also are trained in practical construction methods, project management and contract law. A large part of their time is spent in running projects on site, and in dealing with contractors on their client's behalf.

Technologists

Although their title is not protected by law in the same way as architects, these professionals usually belong to the British Institute of Architectural Technologists (BIAT), which requires its members to be trained and qualified. Academic training is shorter and less broad than it is for architects, but has a more practical edge to it. Aesthetic design skills are not considered essential to qualify, although some technologists develop these through experience.

Surveyors

Surveyors come in many different guises. Their background may be in selling houses, estimating quantities, building construction or property management. Some can and do design houses, with their ability coming from experience rather than training. Again, the use of the title 'surveyor' is not protected, but most surveyors tend to be members of the Royal Institute of Chartered Surveyors (RICS), and must have qualifications to do so.

Contractors

Some building contractors offer house-design services. However, if you use them, it will always be on the condition that you are tied in to using that builder for the construction of the house. You cannot expect independent advice from this person, whose primary duty is to help the contractor for whom he or she works, and you are prevented from inviting competitive prices for the design from anyone else.

Package Company

If you are using a standard kit from a package company, you may not need your own designer. Any design advice on minor changes will be provided by the suppliers, who sometimes employ architects to help them. If you want a bespoke design, some package dealers will provide it, but there is usually a significant – albeit hidden – premium to pay for this convenience, because you remove the opportunity to get competitive prices for the supply of the kit later on.

Unqualified Designers

If you need to check that someone using the title 'architect' is genuine, you can contact the Architects Registration Board, but you can also look at what is written on their letterhead. Someone who is misrepresenting themselves will not use the title architect in writing, since this would be a criminal offence. But anyone who claims that they have the necessary skills and training to design and oversee the construction of a house should be carefully questioned and investigated, regardless of their formal qualifications.

If you are going to need site inspections and certificates, check that your bank or building society will accept the signature of your design professional before you engage them. Qualified professionals usually will not certify someone else's design.

Finding Designers

Realising how important choosing the right designer is for the success of your project, how do you find one? To start with, aim to come up with a shortlist of several candidates, using some or all of the following methods:

Personal Recommendation

This is a good way to find anyone whom you need to provide a service, but most people do not often come across architects – or even self builders who have recently used one to build a house. If encountered in the world of business and commerce, they may not be appropriate for a relatively small-scale domestic project (but they may know someone who is).

The Royal Institute of British Architects

The RIBA have a client services section that will locate local architects for you, or practices with specialist skills such as sustainable design, or straw-bale construction. However, they list most small practices as being suitable for one-off houses, so further investigation may be necessary to establish that they will treat you as a key client, rather than a 'filler' between their regular work. RIBA Client Services can be contacted by phone or through their website, which has an online search facility.

Tel: 020 7307 3700   Website: www.architecture.com

ASBA Architects

Associated Self Build Architects (ASBA) was founded in 1993, to assist people in finding architects with an interest in one-off houses, self build and other domestic work. It has a network of members across the UK, all of whom must be both ARB registered and RIBA members, must carry adequate professional indemnity insurance, and must have a commitment to assisting people with the design and alteration of their own homes. ASBA can be contacted via their website or freephone number.

aSba

ASBA architects specialise in one-off houses.

Tel: 0800 387310   Website: www.asba-architects.org

Yellow Pages and Yell.Com

These are a useful starting point for many people; the problem is the sheer number of consultants listed with minimal information about them. Some of the professional organisations have separate boxes, which list their members in the area covered. Yell.com allows a search by postcode.

Website: www.yell.com

Other Projects In Progress

There will probably be other building work going on near to your site. Consider knocking on the door and asking the householders how it is going, and who created the design for them.

Local Authorities

The codes of practice that planners and building control officers work to prohibit them from putting names forward. Some may give an 'off the record' recommendation, but most will be uncomfortable about doing this. However, the planning register is open for inspection (see 'Finding a Site' section, earlier, for details). This will list the names and addresses of the agents who have submitted applications recently; and your right of public access means that you can take a look at the drawings that they have submitted – an excellent way of building up a picture of whom you would be dealing with.

Specialist exhibitions offer an opportunity to meet architects and inspect their work informally.

Magazines and Shows

The magazines dedicated to self builders and homebuilders are filled with illustrations and case studies of projects, which usually give the name and contact details of the designers. Likewise, national and local exhibitions and shows feature architects and designers. If a practice has gone to the time and trouble to attend a show and make themselves available to prospective clients, this is at least indicates enthusiasm.

Others

There are many other incidental ways of finding your ideal designer. There are several websites that claim to be able help you, but it is important to check what architects have to do to get listed. If the answer is that all they do is pay a fee, there is little value to the recommendation.

Choosing the Right One

Once you have a shortlist, your next task is to narrow it down. Naturally, you will want to do a bit of investigation, but the truth is that the 'gut feeling' often counts the most. Whittle the shortlist down to a maximum of three or four. If you do decide to 'do the rounds' of more potential designers than this the chances of each getting the job are greatly reduced, and they may feel it is a waste of time responding to your enquiry. Busy professionals will not rush to respond to standard letters or emails that have clearly been sent to a large number of companies.

Interviews

Firstly, be sure to spend a little time in the company of the person that you are considering. Don't rush it – whether or not they will spend an hour or two of their time with you is a good indication of how keen they are to do the work. Some will be prepared to visit the site with you and make some initial comments. However, it is unreasonable to expect them to offer repeated consultations or site visits without charge.

Before you visit the practice, ask for some illustrations of previous projects, and ask some leading questions about them at the meeting. Discussing how a previous project developed should give insight into the way that the designer works and thinks.

Formal Qualifications

As mentioned earlier, ask some direct questions about their professional training and qualifications. If you do not understand what the initials after someone's name means, it is perfectly reasonable to ask for them to be explained.

Some letters after a name indicate that exams have been passed, e.g. 'BArch', or 'MBIAT'. Others may simply indicate the payment of the membership fees of an organisation, with no requirement for any qualifications at all.

Experience

Be prepared to ask some searching questions about the experience that the practice has had of one-off houses and working with private clients on their homes. Do they work regularly with people like yourselves, on your scale of project? Do they have technical knowledge and competence as well as design flair? Some architects are talented designers and artists, and have never bothered much with practicalities – and the reverse can also be true of others.

Architects who work on larger projects are used to being supported by a sizeable professional team, including other specialist consultants as well as their immediate colleagues. The budget for a single house can rarely afford this, and the designer must be able to handle a wide range of problems alone, as well as having the sense to know when specialist advice has to be called in.

Attitude

Sometimes designers, particularly architects, are accused of arrogance. There is an explanation for this, and it is not that they are all picked or trained to be like that. Larger projects require a different attitude and approach to small domestic jobs such as yours. Hospitals, big office developments, and the like are hugely complex undertakings and require single-minded determination to conceive and see through to completion. A hard-headed, assertive (but hopefully tactful) approach is essential to prevent the design quality from being sidelined by all the other pressures that come to bear on such projects. These qualities in an architect are what make good buildings possible in a complex working environment.

Some architects cannot switch from this mind-set to the gentler approach needed for domestic projects. There are also a small number of 'signature' architects, who will not take on a client unless they are given full reign to follow their creative intuition. This category produce ground-breaking, breathtaking buildings – but are the sole preserve of very wealthy clients. If the only private house an architect has built is their own, this is not necessarily evidence that they are able to work successfully on the design of someone else's dream project.

The truth is that most architects are approachable, reasonable people, and would not be in business for very long if they were not. Having established that your prospective designer is in this category, you should be listening carefully to how your questions are answered. Do you get straight, clear answers? If you gently criticise one of their previous projects, do you get an overly defensive response? One ability which is not generally included in an architect's formal training is the ability to listen – but it is essential in order for them to be able to work with you.

The Size of the Practice

Generally speaking, typical single house designs are best dealt with by 'sole practitioners' (i.e. one person only), or by small and medium-sized practices. There are a number of reasons for this. A large practice will not put a priority on a comparatively minor project. It may not be managed by anyone senior. In fact, it may even be given to the most junior member of the team, on the mistaken assumption that it will be a relatively straightforward project. This it may be, in construction terms, but there is also a need to communicate well with clients, anticipate and deal with problems efficiently and manage relatively unsophisticated smaller building companies. All this means that, unless a big practice has a good reason to place importance on the job or the budget is a particularly high one, your project may receive less attention than it requires.

A smaller organisation will allow easy access to the directors or partners, who will be monitoring the project daily, if not working on it directly themselves.

ASBA Garside Architects

FRONT ELEVATION

FIRST FLOOR PLAN

DUNELM　　　GROUND FLOOR PLAN　　　**HALE**

Well-presented drawings are a sign of an architect who takes time and trouble over their work.

Completed Work

Aside from asking to see illustrations of previous jobs and talk to past clients, why not ask to see a set of drawings for a typical project? You may be surprised at the range of quality and quantity of work produced by different practices.

Well-presented, concise but thorough drawings and specifications will put the project well on the way to success. If a practice's drawings are badly prepared and drawn, and seem inadequate compared to the others, this is an indication of the quality of service you will get. It is not good enough to rely on the builder to fill in the gaps, or to hope that tricky details can be sorted out on site.

Feasibility Studies

You may wish the architects to work for you for a provisional period before you engage them for the full service. If you ask them to provide some speculative designs without payment, or for a greatly reduced fee, do not be surprised if they refuse. To produce a house design which properly accounts for all the requirements of a client, and also satisfies all the many constraints on the design, is a time-consuming process. Any attempt to gauge the skill of the designer without going through this process misses the point of designing an individual house. Also, you are asking the architect to give away a key part of the service offered – design skill and ingenuity – for little or no payment. Anyone who is familiar with the design process, and the effort that goes into producing a good scheme, will not agree to these unreasonable conditions – but you may get a photocopy of someone else's house design with the label changed. If you want to test the water, one compromise is to engage a designer who has satisfied your selection procedure, on an hourly basis for some feasibility work, with a written agreement that their employment can be terminated if you don't feel that it is working out. Be aware, however, that if you do this before a planning application has been submitted, you cannot then use the design created, the copyright of which is owned by the designer.

Indemnity Insurance

All registered architects are required to maintain professional indemnity insurance (PII) to cover the work that they do in order to use the title. There is not the same compulsion on non-registered designers, although some of the professional organisations require their members to carry insurance. Indemnity insurance premiums are paid annually by the architect's practice, and – in the event of a client demonstrating that professional negligence has occurred, causing a financial loss – the insurers will provide compensation. In other words, if architects make a serious error, which costs you money, they are insured – and the benefit of that insurance is passed on to you.

If you expect to need certification of the building work on site, it is vital to check that the person issuing them is backed by PII, because the funding body may not accept any certificates as valid if this is not in place. The insurance should be at the required level, and bear some relation to the total budget of the project.

Near where you live, or near the site?

If the site is distant from where you live, you will have to decide whether to choose a designer based close to where the building work is going to happen, or within easy reach of your current home. It is probably better to use the former – particularly if a site service is going to be necessary, or if the local planners need careful handling.

Changing Designers

It is not easy to switch from one architect at the design stage, to another once the project is on site. This is because the site architect would have to underwrite the accuracy and reliability of the drawings and specifications, even though they were prepared by someone else. If the architects know and trust each other, it may be possible to arrange this – for example, some members of the ASBA network will agree to do this, with one member providing a client with a design service close to where they live, and another dealing with the construction and site stages.

Appointing An Architect

Paying a Designer

The question of fees and charges should be raised early on in the dialogue by the architect, but if this doesn't happen, make sure that you do it. You should get a proper explanation of the fee structure, and be made fully aware of what you will get for your money – along with the payment terms, expenses charged, etc. If this topic is not dealt with in a businesslike manner, this may not be the right person to be dealing with your finances if a contract-management service is required. Before you agree the fee arrangement, be sure that the level of services being offered is appropriate, and has been agreed and tied into the fee.

Architects may calculate fees by the hour, by a percentage of the build cost, or even by a price per square foot. Which method is used will depend on how much information about your project is available at the time, what level of involvement the architect will have, and the management process to be used – if there is no main contractor, it is impossible to calculate a percentage of the contract value. Typical percentages for the full service range between 6 per cent and 10 per cent depending on the contract value. At the beginning of a project, it is unreasonable and probably unwise to expect a lump-sum fee, since there is no way that the time required for the design can be accurately estimated. Architects have learnt by bitter experience that client sometimes have a higher budget figure in mind that the one that they admit to at the start of a project. Paying too little is as bad a mistake as paying too much, because the quality of service that you receive from your designer will influence the whole of the project. A respected national chain of estate agents has calculated that using an architect to design a house typically adds about 10 per cent to the sale price.

Checklist Menu of Services Offered by Architects and Designers

The following range of services are available from most architects. Some self builders do not require the full service, and, if so, the fees should reflect this.

Brief and Site Appraisal

Before starting work on a design, the architect has to assess the constraints and features of the site, and the needs and aspirations of the clients. A hard look at the budget is also important.

Sketch Design

Preparation of sketch designs, showing plans, site layouts and the external appearance of the building. From these sketches, you develop a design together.

Planning Application

The architect will usually consult with the planning department to assess whether your developing house design is likely to gain planning permission. They then produce detailed drawings of your new house suitable for a planning application. At this stage, major decisions about the appearance of the house are taken.

Building Regulations

A Building Regulations application is made up of a set of drawings, calculations and specifications describing the basic construction of your house. Your house has to conform to Building Regulations in order to receive permission to be built. Usually the architect prepares and submits your Building Regulations application to the local authority, and deals with any queries that are raised.

Tender Package

Drawings and specifications for tender are essential to obtain accurate prices from contractors. These drawings show the precise design and arrangement of the building components, and usually include details such as the stairs, fireplaces and the internal fittings. A specification document shows the quality both of the materials and the construction. The fixtures and fittings are described in detail in the specification, stating the manufacturer and precise component required.

Contractors

An architect can help you to find suitable contractors for your tender list, and see that the process of inviting tenders is carried out correctly. The architect can also prepare building contract documents before work commences.

On Site

The architect can monitor the construction of the house. Regular visits are made to the site in order to check that the works are being carried out in accordance with the contract drawings, without any unnecessary delay and in a professional, workmanlike manner.

Certificates

When a building society provides a mortgage for a self-build project, it may release the money at agreed stages of the work, on receipt of an architect's certificate. This certificate states that a building has been constructed to a satisfactory standard.

Questions to Ask Your Architect/Designer

- Is the designer an architect or a lesser-qualified professional?
- To which professional institutes do the staff members belong?
- How many one-off houses has the practice designed?
- Does the practice have a 'house style'? If so, is it appropriate to your project?
- How many technical/professional staff has the practice got?
- Who will be working on the project, and what is their seniority/experience?
- Can you see examples of completed work and talk to previous clients?
- How soon after receiving an instruction can they start?
- How long should the project take, from now to completion on site?
- How are fees calculated, and how much are they?
- Will they offer to do some feasibility work, and at what charge?
- Does the practice carry professional indemnity insurance?
- Is there a written contract, and, if so, can it be issued in draft and any queries answered?
- What would happen if you asked for a design change that the architect did not agree with?

Appointment Contract

If your designer is an architect, they will be obliged by their registration body to confirm the details of their appointment in writing. Some use standard appointment documents supplied by the RIBA, but others will want to use their own version. Do not accept a simple letter stating the fee. There should be separate appointment document, which you should have a copy of, and you should acknowledge your acceptance of it in writing. You may get away with less than this, but if anything should go wrong, you will find that the absence of agreed terms and conditions could prove an expensive mistake.

A contract with an architect should cover at least the following issues:

- the exact level of service being commissioned
- who instructs the architect
- who will be engaging consultants such as the engineer
- how fees are calculated, and whether VAT is due
- expenses, and how much they are (printing costs alone can be several hundred pounds for a large house design)
- when you will be invoiced and how long you will have to pay
- what happens if you are unhappy with something and don't wish to pay the amount invoiced
- how you can terminate the agreement, and what reasons you can have to do this
- who owns the copyright to the design of your house
- if a dispute arises between you, how it would be settled
- who you can complain to if you feel that the required standards of professional conduct have not been met

The reason that professional bodies like the RIBA insist their members have written agreements like this is because it reduces the likelihood of any misunderstandings occurring, and it ensures that clients of their members are properly informed of their rights at the start of a project.

Designing Your House

A successful house design will combine your budget, your requirements and the constraints of the site in an effective way. It is the combination of these three elements that give a design impetus, and make the house individual and unique. By the time you start working on the house design, you should have a fairly good idea of each of them, and your first discussion will probably revolve around the relationship between them and where you are prepared to compromise. The success of the design will depend as much on the work that you have done before this point as it will on what you and your architect do next.

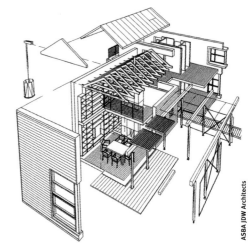

A good architect will create a three-dimensional design centred on your requirements.

Preparing for the First Design Meeting
Budget

At this stage – having found the site, carried out some site investigations, and appointed your designer – you should have a fairly good idea of how much you can afford to spend on the building. It is time to review the budget and confirm whether the figures still stack up, and to discuss in detail with your designer where you want to spend your money. At this point, you will have to work to some estimated cost per square foot, or per square metre, and agree the assumptions that you are making.

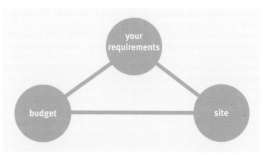

The three major influences on the design of an individual house.

Check that build costs have not altered since your initial calculations, either as a result of having bought in a different area or general inflation over the time that has passed since you first did them.

However tempting it is to commit all the money available in the calculation of the floor area you can afford, resist it. Build costs always go up as the design process develops – the principal reason being that more and more desirable things get added. A more subtle effect occurs when you hit knotty space-planning problems. The easy solution is usually to add more space – making a corridor a bit longer, the hallway a bit bigger, or a room slightly wider can make a layout work that otherwise would be impractical. The cumulative effect, however, can be that by the end of the initial sketch design the whole house has increased in size significantly. So it is essential that your designer keeps you informed of the floor area of any proposals that are put forward for your comments, and that you are clear in your own mind that a bigger building will almost certainly mean a bigger bill for you.

Site

By the time you come to the design stage, you should at least have your site 'under offer' if not already purchased. It is essential, if you want to avoid wasted effort and money, that you are reasonably sure that the site is going to be yours before you start designing. If there is some doubt, it may be prudent to wait until you are certain that you will be able to acquire the plot. Although you may be able to use some of the ideas generated even if you have to switch to a new site, a lot of time and expense will have been wasted. Once a site analysis has been completed (as described in 'Assessing a Site', earlier), this must be fed into the design.

Your Requirements

If you have thought carefully about what you need from the new house, possibly by using the system of forms suggested in this book, you designer should be well set up to begin the design process. However you do it, the most important thing is that you communicate as much of this information as possible, as early as possible, to your architect.

Be open to suggestions from the architect as to how you may modify your ideas to improve the design, and keep to your budget. Good designers do not just take the brief from you and stick to it unthinkingly; they question it. This does not mean that they are criticising you, or suggesting that you are wrong. Designer are trained to think laterally, and a fundamental part of the design process is to try to generate ideas, which often have to be sketched out to tell whether or not they are going to work. Discussing why a proposal is wrong can be quickly followed by a revised version that provides an elegant solution to a problem.

It may only be obvious that a particular idea is unworkable once it has been accurately drawn to scale. The alternative is to insist that the brief is adhered to, and there are two disadvantages to this way of working. One is that you miss the once-and-only opportunity to test out ideas on paper before they end up in solid brickwork, and the other is that it is almost universally true that some of the demands of the brief are impossible to satisfy when confronted with the budget, site and reality of designing a workable building. Architects, faced with the latter situation, should really refuse to proceed, but this is a lot to ask if they may not get paid by a client who is disgruntled as a result of their honest criticism.

The First Design Meeting

1. Ensure that the budget is updated and the build cost is confirmed.
2. Agree an estimate of the price per sq m or sq ft that will be used as a basis for the design.
3. Ensure that the designer has visited the site prior to the meeting.
4. Decide on the principal contacts for your family and for the architects.
5. Confirm details of your fax or email, if available.
6. Agree the expected timetable for the design process.
7. Hand over documents describing the brief to the architects.
8. Discuss the design principles and run through the brief to highlight important requirements.

Aspects of Design

There are a multiplicity of influences on the way that a building is designed, and, at its best, the design process involves a free flow of ideas between client and architect. The following are just some of the factors that may have a role to play in your design.

The Concept

This a favourite word of many architects. It implies that any design can be distilled down to a basic big idea, which is followed through at all levels. Most of the great architects have followed this line of thought, and it has resulted in some truly wonderful buildings. A concept may be expressed as a simple line-drawing indicating a particular form of building, or a statement of the thinking behind the design. The practical problem is that, for most designs, there has to be an element of compromise between the many issues that compete for priority, but there is no reason why you shouldn't have a main concept for your house. For example, it might be a particularly favoured photo from a magazine, or a statement such as 'our home must be like a country cottage' or 'our house will be a place that will make people say "Wow!" when they see it' or 'it will be a place to relax and enjoy ourselves'. If you have an overriding idea like this, and repeat it to yourselves as the design develops, it will help to remind you why you are doing it.

Style Types

The vast majority of houses built in the UK are in a style that could be called 'neo-vernacular' – that is, modern versions of traditional building styles. These house designs sometimes end up looking bland, because they are simply standard boxes with imitations of traditional features clipped on to them, or they have been reproduced with only minor changes across a large estate. All traditional buildings derive their style from the builders making the best use of the limited range of materials available. In the past, the availability of local building materials, and what could be done with them, decided the appearance of the building.

For example, if only plain clay tiles were available, the roof pitch could not go much below 35°, and ordinary softwood can only span up to about 6 m. So a modern house that has concrete tiles at a

These house designs are based on radically different concepts of how they should look.

pitch of 30°, spanning 10 or 12 m, will look wrong no matter how much it is dressed up to appear 'traditional'. The same rules apply to windows, which should be in smaller panes, and – for a true traditionalist – single-glazed (although the latter option has now been made virtually impossible by Building Regulations). Likewise, a timber-framed building based on a traditional Essex yeoman's house will not look right in an area like Cumbria, where good quality building stone was easier to obtain than wood. There are plenty of good sources of reference that analyse vernacular architecture and suggest the principles to follow when designing new buildings.

Some buildings take traditional styles as their inspiration.

Most other house designs tend to be 'derivative' – that is they imitate a style from history, typically Georgian, Victorian, Edwardian or Arts & Crafts. Thanks to a few pioneering self builders, contemporary house designs are occasionally built – some which are unique in the way that they use modern materials. In fact, the latter group have usually led the fashion for house style, with housing developers following a long way behind. If you wish to build your home in an individual style it is essential to use an architect, and you may meet resistance both from neighbours and the conservative-minded planning system in the UK.

Contemporary designs often use materials in interesting ways.

The Site

The importance of the site in the design process should hopefully be clear from the earlier section on 'Assessing a Site'. Views off and on to the plot, planning restrictions, neighbouring buildings, and other factors can all affect the final design. Where a site has particular constraints, a creative design can use them to make an interesting and individual house.

The approach to a house will set the tone of the property, before anyone has even gone into it. The way to the front door should be easy to identify from the edge of the site, and the point of entry into the house should be apparent as someone walks towards it. For example, the front door can be positioned on the centre-line of the front elevation, or indicated by a porch or change in the landscaping around it.

If a site has a steep slope, it can be used to create different levels inside.

The easiest way to draw attention to the front door is to put it in the centre of a symmetrical façade, and surround it with a porch.

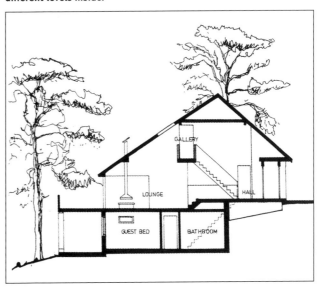

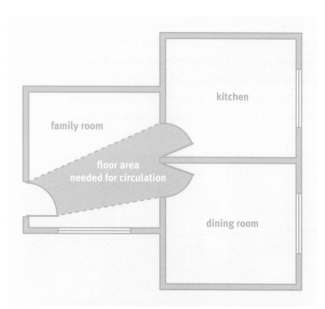

If it is planned badly, and you have to move through one room to get to others, the space may become useless.

For this house, the circulation areas are a key feature of its design.

Circulation

A design decision that has to be made early is how the space will be allocated within the plan, and which rooms will get priority. As part of this, the size of the hall, landing and corridors is an important factor. One way of looking at this is to maximise the size of the rooms by reducing the area given up to circulation. Taken to its extreme, this will result in cramped halls and staircases, which will give the impression of a meanly planned house as soon as visitors walk in the door. It also tends to result in areas of rooms being given up to circulation instead, making them less comfortable to use, and reducing their useful area.

The alternative view is to commit a disproportionate amount of space to the hall and landing, which conveys a feeling of spaciousness and luxury. Subconsciously, if you can afford to 'waste' space on circulation, it suggests an expensive property.

The alternative to the traditional British house plan is to adopt an 'open-plan' approach, and do away with many of the distinctions between rooms and circulation altogether. Open-plan designs are particularly suited to smaller houses because they

Open-plan design can make limited space seem much bigger than it really is.

give the illusion of plenty of space, and lend a contemporary feel to their design. With modern levels of insulation and underfloor heating, there is no need to worry about draughts – but these kinds of house plans are not ideal for privacy.

The roof void of a house can be used to form unusual spaces.

Where building land is restricted, basements are worth the investment.

Windows don't have to be rectangular.

Roof space

One way to increase the potential size of the house is to use the roof space. This is a particularly useful option if the planners have restricted the ridge height for some reason, and is also quite cost-effective. Although you have to strengthen the ceiling joists, use more expensive insulation between the rafters, and also fit out and decorate the attic as habitable space, you get the external structure – the roof – for free.

Basements

Instead of going up to find more room, you could also consider going down, in the form of a basement. Basements are less economical than using the roof void, and their quality of space is not suited for use as bedrooms or living rooms. However, if your foundations have to be deeper than normal due to site constraints, or if the site is very small relative to the size of house you want to build, they have many benefits. There is even a thriving market for companies that will excavate under existing homes to create basements. In areas like London, where land is costly, it is cheaper to pay out £50,000 or £60,000 to add a basement than it is to try to buy a bigger house.

Windows and Natural Light

The location of the windows in each room will be decided by blending the requirements of the occupants and the effect of the site outside. Windows offer views in as well as views out, so privacy will probably be a factor in deciding where the rooms and their windows are positioned. But windows are also a source of ventilation and natural light. By far the brightest part of a view out of a window is the sky, so the amount of light that comes through a window is determined by how much sky is visible through it, which is why roof lights add an extra feeling of quality to a room. Apart from trying to maximise the amount of natural light in a room, arranging windows so that the daylight comes from more than one direction makes the play of light and shadows more interesting. Although most people are not aware of this effect, they do tend to feel more relaxed in a room that has windows on more than one wall.

The Future

Hopefully, you will have a reasonable idea of how long you expect to live in your new home. If you expect to live long enough for a change in family circumstances, this ought to be allowed for in the design and construction of the house.

A classic example is the recently retired couple who are fit and well, and who do not intend to move out of their home. It is advisable for them to allow for wheelchair use throughout the house, by ensuring that the doors and toilet areas are generously proportioned. Some even allocate a ground-floor room as a future bedroom, in case either of them becomes too frail to get upstairs, and put the drainage in ready for a connecting ground floor en suite bathroom. Even if the couple themselves are fortunate enough to stay fit and healthy, the chances that one of their friends or family will develop some kind of impairment are high.

There are extensive provisions that can be made to make use of the house easier for the blind or partially sighted, the deaf, arthritis suffers, wheelchair users, etc. Anyone who wants to include any of these should seek advice early in the design.

The Building Regulations make some provision for use by disabled people compulsory. They are fairly basic for one-off houses and many disabled people and experts consider them inadequate.

At the other end of the age spectrum, a young couple who expect to have children once they are settled might choose to build the attic and staircase in such a way that rooms-in-the-roof can be created with relative ease if necessary. Alternatively, they may include a future extension in the design, and even get planning approval for it, so that extra space can be added as the family expands. There are countless other examples – each family will have their own aspirations for the future, and many can be catered for in the way the house is designed

A well-designed house can work with the landscape, rather than against it.

Sustainable Building

This is the current buzzword for what used to be known as 'green' or 'eco-friendly' design. The range of design techniques, materials and products that can be used to make a house more sustainable is wide, enough to easily fill several books alone. There are some basic things that can be done as part of the design to reduce the energy requirements of the building. The ultimate objective of sustainable design has been described as 'living lightly on the land', i.e. making as little impact on the environment as possible.

Some things you can do to make your house more 'green'

- Site the house near to public transport routes, and use them.
- Put more glass on the south-facing side than the north, making use of free heat from the sun.
- Don't use too much glass, and put where it will reduce the need for artificial light.
- Make the house well-insulated (this usually causes the walls to be thicker).
- Use materials that are from renewable sources, such as softwood.
- Use a material that recycles waste, such as concrete blocks, or softwood 'I beams'.
- Store rainwater in an underground sump, and pump it up to water the garden or flush the toilets.
- Specify an energy-efficient boiler, e.g. a gas condensing boiler.

- Consider alternative methods for energy supply, e.g. solar panels, or geothermal heat – but be aware of the long 'payback' time.
- Use low-energy lighting throughout the house.
- Fit 'intelligent' controls to the heating, lighting and appliances, to minimise waste.
- Find our how the materials that are proposed to be used for the house are made, and check whether they waste resources or add to the carbon in the atmosphere.

The Healthy House

A development of the thinking behind sustainability is the idea that some designs, layouts and materials incorporated into a house can be better for the occupants' health than others. Allergy-free houses cater for people with asthma or similar allergic reactions. They use natural materials in preference to man-made, and may use air-filtration systems to reduce dust. Some of the science is disputed, such as the idea that the small amounts of gas given off by certain plastics is going to be harmful to inhabitants. But a lot of the ideas go back to good principles of design, such as using sun, shade and natural light to lend a feeling of well-being, or making bedrooms restful places to be in.

Just because it is built to sustainable principles, a house doesn't need to look 'wacky' or be built in an extraordinary way. This house is totally self sufficient, and has been designed to function with no connections to any mains services.

This house, built in Milton Keynes, was also designed to eco-friendly principles, but has a radically different appearance to the house shown above.

Photo: Nigel Rigden/Homebuilding & Renovating

Good lighting can redefine a building at night-time.

Artificial Light

The success or otherwise of a room design at night-time can be decided by the way that it is lit. Apart from the obvious items, like ceiling-mounted pendants or wall-mounted uplighters, there are plenty of possibilities for using lights to set style and mood. Mini-spots, track lighting, standard lamps, lampshades and fibre optics can all be used to great effect. More sophisticated houses have two or three designs for the lights in a room, depending on whether people are sitting on their own with a book, watching TV or entertaining friends, and these can be controlled by a programmable switch.

If you want a master-class in how to use artificial light to make a room look good, visit a show home by one of the good-quality developers. They often use lighting to help sell their properties to customers, and sometimes to conceal poor daylighting levels.

Resist the temptation to leave the lighting design until the rooms are complete. It is difficult to visualise how it will work on plans, but it is possible to make some guesses, to ensure that you have allowed enough in your budget. Once the rooms are ready for 'first fix', you can go around and finalise where the lights are actually to go.

Precast concrete floors give the best possible sound insulation.

Noise

How intrusive noise can be is very subjective. Someone who has lived next to a railway line all their life may not notice it. City-dwellers who move to the countryside may find the relative silence oppressive. Noise within the house can be controlled by the positioning of rooms from which it emanates away from rooms which would find it a nuisance, e.g. the teenage kids' bedrooms can be kept apart from Mum and Dad by putting bathrooms, or a corridor, between them. The construction of the house will also have a role to play, because the best way to reduce sound transmission is mass. In other words, put something heavy – like a masonry wall – between you and the source of noise.

If you use a suspended timber floor, there will be more noise filtering through between floors, and any upper-storey blockwork walls will have to be positioned so that they can be either built off masonry walls on the ground floor, or supported on steel beams. If you can afford to use precast concrete for the upper floors, this will allow you to use blockwork walls for all the bedrooms without worrying about supporting them below – giving good sound-reduction all round.

External noise can be harder to deal with, but one way is to site rooms where noise is less of a problem – like putting bathrooms and kitchens along the side of the house closest to a busy road. Triple glazing can help, but not in summer when the windows need to be opened. The extreme, and definitely 'unsustainable', solution is to fit an air-conditioning system, so that the windows can be kept closed even when it is hot outside.

Safety/Fire

When they are designing their dream home, most people prefer not to think about the bad things that can happen in life, but the design should take account of safety issues, and particularly escape in case of fire – especially if the house is going to be used by the elderly, the infirm, or young children. Fatal accidents are more common at home than in any other situation.

Again, there are basic regulations that ensure that the house has upper-storey windows that can be used for escape in an emergency, and that houses with more than one floor above ground level have their landings and stairways fire-protected. These basic precautions can easily be improved upon, especially if they are considered at the design stage. For example, you should fit more than the minimum number of smoke alarms required, and ensure that there are several safe routes out of the house – even consider some soft landscaping, in the event of someone having to jump out of a window. An increasingly popular option is for domestic sprinkler systems, on the grounds that once one is fitted the chances of anyone dying in a house fire are negligible, and damage to property is minimised.

Sometimes, basic design decisions can make a house either more or less safe to live in. For example, if there are large areas of glazing at high level, how will they be cleaned and the frames repainted? If there are small changes in level within the same floor, are they clearly visible enough to prevent anyone tripping on them? Are the doors planned to reduce the risk of people colliding if they are used at the same time?

Security

Security must be considered by anyone who builds their own home. There are two approaches – either defend or expose vulnerable areas. Which one you use may partly depend on where the house is located. The defensive method involves things like high walls, security gates, video cameras and even security shutters on the windows. This might be used in isolated rural areas, or on large sites where there are unlikely to be many people around to notice suspicious characters trying to force their way into the house. The disadvantage is that the features are highly visible, and it is a good way to announce to the world that you think you have something worth stealing.

The alternative method is to open out the areas most likely to be points of attack, or routes of approach, to public view. This could mean that the front garden is open, with the whole of the front of the house visible to neighbours and passers-by. Used in conjunction with security lights, which detect movement, it can be more effective that barbed wire in keeping out intruders who do not want to be seen, but it relies on neighbours being close at hand.

You may use either of the above on different sides of the house in combination, depending on their circumstances.

High railings combine both the above ideas, because they prevent easy access as well as allowing a view through to the house beyond, but your house may look more like a prison than a home as a result.

Storage

However much storage is allowed for at the design stage, once the house is built you will probably discover that it is inadequate. But, often, house design does not allow anything at all in the plans, assuming that it will be created by installing wardrobes, fitted furniture, etc. Many houses built by developers are totally inadequate in this area because they use the space to make the rooms bigger, and therefore help to sell the house before it is occupied. Otherwise 'dead' spaces, such as those under the staircase, can be allocated for storage, but it is a good idea to make sure that

The potter who lives in this house has adapted the attic for storage.

at least one space is created on the first floor as an airing cupboard. Even if there will not be a hot-water cylinder, a small radiator can be provided to keep it warm and dry.

A simple card model to 1:100 scale of a proposed design will help you visualise the spaces that will be created, particularly if you can add something to represent a human figure.

Designing the Rooms

Once you have decided on an overall layout, you need to consider the design and features of the individual rooms. It is not within the remit of this book to cover interior design in any detail, but the characteristics of each room start to be laid down at the planning stage, and, in turn, the way each space is designed will affect the design of the house as a whole. Remember, these do not have to be separate areas divided by walls – they can easily be joined together to form larger spaces.

Hall

As mentioned before, the entrance hall will set the tone of the whole house as visitors step across the threshold. Ideas to try to work in include: as much double-height space as you can afford, by giving up some of the upper-floor areas to void; lots of natural light; and avoiding making the hall too narrow. A few hundred millimetres saved on plan, and allocated instead to adjoining rooms, can have a big effect on how spacious the hall feels. A minimum width of, say, 1200 mm is recommended, but try to arrange for at least part of the hallway to be much wider than this.

Staircase

Potentially, the stair has the most exciting possibilities to offer to a designer, because of the double height, change in level and design options for the stairs themselves. Try to avoid designing to the minimum sizes required by the Building Regulations. If you do, it may look cramped and be steep to climb, and people with large feet will find it uncomfortable. At an early stage in the design, allow plenty of space for the staircase, because, once the plan is firmed up, it will be too late to make it larger. A window on to the stairwell at upper-floor level, or even a rooflight, will transform the quality of the space by providing natural light and views. If you have the budget, staircases do not have to be rectilinear. Many houses have been leant an air of grandeur by using the skills of local carpenters to design and build an elegant,

The hallway often defines the character of the interior of a house.

Stairways and landings should be an integral part of a house design.

curved handrail and stair. There are also many materials that can be used, depending on the effect that is required. Steel, glass, stone and brick have all been used successfully to form handrails, treads and risers.

Steps do not have to be used only to get between floors. They can also be used together with floor and ceiling-level changes within each storey, particularly to give interest and divide larger open-plan rooms – provided attention is paid to the needs of wheelchair users and ambulant disabled people.

Living Room or Lounge

This is often the space that people use to project their chosen image to visitors, being a more formal room than some of the others, and the area where guests are most likely to be entertained. This is also the room most likely to contain a favourite feature of many people who build their own home – a real fireplace. It is vital to plan the furniture that will go in this room at as early a stage as possible in the design process. This

Living rooms can be used to project an image of yourself to guests.

because there will be a direct effect on the size and proportions of the room. If there is going to be a fireplace, be sure that it is not too large for the room – many living rooms have been spoiled by a huge inglenook that would have looked at home in a baronial hall, but which totally dominates a relatively narrow, average-sized lounge.

Family Room

It is not easy to define this room; it means different things to different people. But it could be described as a cross between a children's playroom and an informal eating area. Its relationship with other spaces is usually determined by the age of the family. It seems to work well when it opens off the kitchen, particularly where there are young children who need to be supervised and kept entertained whilst domestic chores are carried out. If it can have a direct relationship with the garden, perhaps in the form of French windows, this is also a benefit.

Kitchen

In some households, particularly those of busy young professional couples, the kitchen is the least used of the principal ground-floor rooms. Meals are frequently eaten out, or prepared in minutes with the help of a microwave. For others, often families with children, the kitchen is the focal point of the house. It is used for eating, chatting to friends, watching TV, cooking and

A kitchen may be just somewhere to heat up a meal, or somewhere to socialise with your family and friends.

washing, and for homework. Which of these categories you expect to be in will influence the size and shape of your kitchen, but also its location in relation to the rest of the house. The family will probably want it to be centrally placed – possibly connected to a dining room, family room, and a conservatory – as well as having a direct link with the entrance hall.

It is a good idea to get some kitchen designs sketched out (and costed) by a kitchen supplier before the final plan is agreed. Specialist designers can usually offer an insight into the layout that may lead to the alteration of the proportions of the room, or the need for a window to be repositioned to allow an extra feature to be squeezed into the plan.

> *The activities in the kitchen require a lot of circulation space around the units. Sometimes this can double up as circulation across the room, thus saving space.*

Utility Rooms

The need for large utility rooms has declined, particularly as washing machines have got quieter. They can, however, be a useful wet area, or somewhere to dump muddy boots before going into the rest of the house. Like the kitchen, the long, thin space needed to access cupboards and the washing machine can also serve as a corridor.

> *If you only plan to use the utility room for washing and drying clothes, why not put it on the first floor of the house? This will save carrying the clothes downstairs to be washed, and up again when they are dry.*

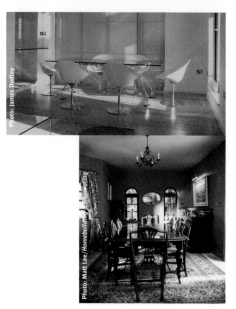

Two examples of different styles of dining room.

Dining Room

The days of the traditional dining room may be numbered. Modern, casual lifestyles have little demand for this rather formal space that is sometimes only used once a year to entertain the boss, and then serves as a homework room-cum-study for the rest of the time. If you decide that you do need one, the obvious thing to check in the design is that a decent table will fit in it, with sufficient circulation space around to avoid guests being nudged in the back every time someone gets up to leave the room. This area tends to be used mainly in the evening, so views out and daylight may not be as vital as in some of the other spaces, which means that it can be situated in areas which would be less suitable for other uses.

Study/Home Office

More and more people do at least some of their work at home. With the increased availability of advanced information technology, the number of full-time home workers is growing rapidly. Excepting those who are planning to retire to their dream home, most people will need to include an area for this kind of activity. If business visitors are expected, it is vital to have the office closely associated with the front door, or even to have a separate entrance, to avoid conflict between your private and business lives.

> *If you intend to employ other people to work with you at your home, or expect to have a lot of business visitors, you will probably need planning approval, since these things are considered by the planners to be a 'material change' from domestic use.*

WC

Care needs to be taken when positioning the 'smallest room'. There has to be at least one WC on the ground floor, because the Building Regulations require it – and they also insist that it is big enough to be used by someone in a wheelchair. Ideally, the WC should not be sited adjacent to the main front door, or be one of the first things that visitors see (or worse, hear) as they approach the house

– and it should have walls that are good sound insulators. In some circumstances guests sitting in a dining room, lounge or similar space, underneath a first-floor WC will be treated to the sound of a flushing toilet each time it is used. Because modern ventilation methods are so efficient, there is no need to have a window into a WC, and it can even open on to a kitchen (which used to be against regulations). This may be expedient, even if not desirable.

Conservatories and Sun Rooms

Conservatories are a very popular choice for people improving their homes, since they add space and light with minimum disruption to an existing house. Their limitations are that they can overheat in summer, be too cold to use in winter, and are expensive to heat. If you are building a house from scratch, the conservatory can be designed to look like part of the house, rather than an afterthought. An alternative approach is to have a solid, insulated roof with roof lights, and glazed walls. The advantage of this approach is that the high-angle summer sun is blocked out by the roof, whilst the low-angle winter sun is allowed in through the walls. However, a quirk of the Building Regulations means that conservatories are defined as such by their translucent roof, and are exempt from heat-loss restrictions, but sun rooms are not and you have to compensate for the heat lost through the glazed walls by increasing insulation levels in the rest of the house.

This conservatory has been integrated into the dining room design.

This conservatory is also the entrance porch.

Garage

The main decision is whether to have an attached or detached garage. The former is cheaper to build, can be entered without going outside the house, and allows the opportunity to use the space above as a bedroom – also a very cost-effective idea. If a garage is detached, it can act as a contingency in the budget, in that building it can be postponed to save money without affecting the rest of the design. Estate agents say that a garage adds value to a house beyond the cost of building it – but very few people seem to keep their cars in them, their main use being for storage. Whether or not you will keep cars in the garage, make sure its size relates to the size and cost of the house. A single garage, suitable for modest private cars may be appropriate for a three-bedroom house, whereas only a generously proportioned double or triple garage is acceptable for a five or six-bedroom property.

When deciding on a garage, allow space to open the car doors as well as park. Some unwary self builders have not anticipated this potential problem until they have parked their car in the finished building, and tried to get out of it.

Master Bedroom

A consistent complaint about most of the UK housing stock is that the bedrooms are too small. This is because houses are valued by agents according to how many bedrooms they have, rather than their size. Consequently, most individually built homes tend to have larger bedrooms generally, and the master bedroom is very often significantly bigger than normal. Extra spaces off it, such as dressing rooms and en suite bathrooms, are also more common in self-build homes.

Other Bedrooms

The ideal layout for the upper floors is to arrange the bedrooms so that they are separated from each other by bathrooms, WCs, landings, etc. to help sound insulation and improve privacy. If at all possible, the main walls should be masonry, which means either using concrete floors, structural steel, or planning solid ground-floor walls to coincide with the upper-storey walls. Another classic problem for families who involve their children in the design process is trying to ensure that their bedrooms are the same size as each other and have a similar aspect – a complex system of trade-offs and bribes is sometimes needed to preserve family harmony.

This roof space makes an ideal bedroom.

En Suite Bathrooms

Apart from the master bedroom, some of the other rooms may have en suite bathrooms. If they all have access to one, there is no need for a separate bathroom. A compromise is to have an en suite shared between two bedrooms, with two lockable doors. It is preferable to have a window in an en suite, but not essential, and compromising on this can help with planning the layout of the upper floors.

Left: Clever use of a mirror makes this bathroom appear larger.
Right: Artificial lighting can be used to soften the clinical feeling of a bathroom.

Bathroom

It is possible to plan very compact bathrooms, to minimise the space needed and free it up for use elsewhere. If your family do not spend a lot of time there, this is a sensible economy. Alternatively, some people consider a large, luxurious bathroom essential.

Summary

Although the construction principles are fairly straightforward, taking account of all your requirements – and turning them into a cost-effective building that make best use of a site – can be quite a complex business. But if you have a clear idea of what is most important to you, and have realistic expectations, perseverance will pay off. At the end of this process you will have a finished set of drawings, which describe the floor plans, the outside appearance and how the building occupies the site. You are ready for the next stage, which is to submit for planning approval.

The design of the building does not stop at this stage, but continues right up until the house is finally completed on site. Keep the principles for the design that you have worked out in mind, and ensure that these are followed through into the detailed design and construction.

What to Get Right in the Design Process

- communication between client and architect
- cost awareness by the architect
- cost awareness by the client
- architect to listen carefully to the client's requirements
- client to listen to, and consider carefully, the advice of the architect
- thorough brief to be prepared by client
- architect to research the site and project fully
- architect to be used to working for private clients
- both to be open to alternatives that may develop

Getting Planning Permission

Of all the tasks to be completed in the mission of getting a house designed and built, getting planning approval is the one over which you have least control. For the most part, you are in the hands of the local authority, and the procedure will run at its own pace, regardless of your anxiety to move forward as quickly as possible. In turn, the planning authority will consult many other people and organisations, and these will all get the opportunity to try to influence the outcome of the application. A decision is supposed to be arrived at within eight weeks of the application being registered, but the complexities of reconciling all the competing interests – and the high workload of the planning officers – mean that it often takes much longer. Despite your efforts, you may get a refusal and have to lodge an appeal – which may, in turn, be rejected.

There are many things that you can do to make your encounter with the planning system less painful, but you should never assume that getting planning approval is going to be automatic, and always allow a contingency in the programme for the process to overrun.

Table 11: Ideal Timescale of a Planning Application.				
Pre-planning negotiations	Submission and Logging of application	Consultations	Negotiation/discussion and preparation of report	Decision
	← 3 - 4 weeks →		← 3 - 4 weeks →	

Why you must get it right

Planning approval of the house that you want to be built must be in place before any building work starts, and you must build in accordance with the approved drawings and comply with any planning conditions. If you make any changes to the design that significantly affect the outside of the building, the revised drawings should be sent to the planning authority for them to approve as amendments. If the changes are significant in planning terms, a fresh application may have to be submitted. There are draconian powers available to make sure you do all this, so nothing should be built unless there is no doubt that it has been approved, because if any part of the design does not get approval, you could be made to demolish it.

The different types of planning approval and their implications are explained in the earlier section on 'Assessing a Site', because that is when you need to familiarise yourself with them. Assuming that you and your advisors have fully checked out the site, someone should have already made contact with the planning authority and the site should have at least outline approval in place. Consequently, assuming that you are not going to build a house to a design prepared for someone else, you will need to submit either an application for approval of Reserved Matters (i.e. those aspects of the design not included in the original application) if the approval in place is outline, or for full permission if the approval in place is detailed, but for another design.

If the house is to be built in the grounds of a listed building, or involves the demolition of a structure in a Conservation Area, you will have to submit separate, but simultaneous, applications for consent for these procedures as well.

Timing

The ideal situation is not to actually buy the property until you have got planning approval for your own house design in place. To do this, you will have to ask the vendor to wait several months, which they may not be prepared to do if there are other buyers waiting in the wings. You can offer a consideration (payment) to them for waiting until your permission to come through, but even this may not be able to compete with an immediate payment from someone else. Often, the only thing to do is to hope that your initial, encouraging discussions with the planners bear fruit, and stump up the money for the site. The worst-case scenario is that you will have to sell the site because you don't get the permission you need. Your loss is then the time and money spent acquiring the site and having a design prepared.

Inside the Mind of a Planner

Although it sometimes feels like there is some kind of personal or hidden agenda at work when a planning officer is less than enthusiastic about your design, this is extremely rare. Sometimes a planner will be aware of discussions regarding other proposed applications, which are confidential, and this may cause them to be a bit evasive. Many misunderstandings occur between applicant and planning authority because the former misunderstands the rationale that the latter applies when making a decision. Planners are governed by a set of bureaucratic rules that may not seem logical from the outside. If you understand these rules, you can deal with the planners on their own terms and increase the likelihood of a successful result. The following are just a few of the concerns that will be playing on the mind of the planning officer:

Planning history of the site.

You should already know what applications have been submitted, and how they were received by the planners and the community, well before this stage. If there is a planning history attached to your plot, or its immediate area, the officer will know of it too, and it might influence how you are received and treated. For example, one self builder was received by a planning officer with what seemed like baffling hostility – until it became clear that a developer's application for a single house on a nearby site, which was initially granted, had been followed up by an application for three houses on the same site, which eventually was granted on appeal to the fury of the local community and the embarrassment of the officer concerned. Once he was convinced that he was dealing with a family, who would be living in the house for many years, his attitude changed completely.

All planning approvals are a matter of public record, and the plans for previously approved houses can be inspected at the local planning department. A bit of research there can give you a good idea of what is likely to be acceptable. Some records are also available on the Internet.

Planning Policy

The planning policy for an area, as set out in the Local Plan or Draft Local Plan, may suggest how certain kinds of application are to be treated. If you put an application in for a larger house on a site with approval for two smaller houses, or several flats, it may seem reasonable to you – because the development is less intensive – but the Local Plan may say that there are too many big houses and not enough smaller 'affordable' homes in the area. Some Local Plans are so drafted that the presumption is against all new houses – where, for example, there has been migration out of the area and existing houses are empty. The planning departments also have to take account of planning policy at county, regional and national levels.

Nottingham City Local Plan.

More confusion can result because, as mentioned before, planning policy is rarely static. It is constantly being reviewed, amended and altered. So if you ask to do something that has been done to the house across the road, it is a valid defence for the planning officer to state that it was done several years ago and is now 'contrary to current policy'.

Impact on Surroundings

In Areas of Outstanding Natural Beauty, in Conservation Areas, or near listed buildings it is obvious that you must respect the adjoining buildings and environment. However, there may also be a concern as to how the new design affects the setting as seen from a distance, sometimes even miles away if views of it are still possible. So, although you may feel that there is no impact on immediate neighbours or surroundings, the planner may be worrying about the effect on the landscape as seen from the nearest hill.

This house was built in the heart of a National Park, a very sensitive planning area. It was carefully designed to follow and blend in with the landscape, and was built using local stone.

Size, Shape, Massing

The architect may have gone to a great deal of trouble to match the detailing and materials of the building to the local style, but if the size and shape are alien, no amount of dressing up will make it look right.

Neighbours

In theory, the authority should not reject your application just because the neighbours, or any influential interest groups, do not like it. The neighbours have to raise objections based on planning criteria, which must then be objectively assessed. The reality is that if there are significant objections – and especially if, as a result, local councillors become involved – your application will be handled more carefully, to ensure that there cannot be any criticism of the procedure followed. The case officer will be more reluctant to stick his or her neck out and agree things on the spot, and any negotiations will take longer as a result.

Privacy is a big issue with neighbours, which is why balconies must be carefully positioned, like this one, to avoid allowing a grandstand view into the neighbouring garden.

Always go and see immediate neighbours with the plans before submitting an application. If you don't the first thing they will learn of it is a letter from the council stating that an application has been made, but providing no other information. In the absence of any drawings, the tendency is to picture the worst, and they will be thinking negatively before they get to the town hall to view the plans. If they have met you, and can see that you are going to be decent neighbours, they may be put at ease – and at least you will be forewarned if their opposition is going to be implacable. It is also worth noting that if your plans are refused, the alternative may be a developer who will not be living in the area after the house is built, and who will be less concerned about how they feel about it.

Even if you secure the support of the planning department, the final decision may be made by the Planning Committee, and they may ignore any advice and refuse it anyway – for 'political reasons'.

Relevant local amenity societies and Parish Councils are usually consulted when an application is made, and will be asked to comment on your design. They are usually happy to allow you to present the design for discussion before the application is made. If they support it, the application will have fewer problems than if they oppose it.

Precedent

At the back of every planning officer's mind is always the question of whether something similar to your proposal has been granted in the past, and whether granting approval will unintentionally give someone a case for doing something the planning department are trying to restrict in the future. If they grant approval for you to remove a couple of protected trees to project your building, will this assist a developer who wants to cut down several to allow a bigger development, leading to the collapse of a carefully worked-out strategy to preserve an area of natural woodland? If they agree to you having one less car-parking space on your site, will anyone building other houses in the area be able to demand the same treatment? The only way round the risk of setting an unwanted precedent is to prove that your case is special, and that there are unique reasons in your case that will not apply to any other sites in the area.

Initial Consultations and Meetings

Planning officers are members of your project team – whether you like it or not – so, to get the best results, it is sensible to treat them as such. They should be consulted as a matter of course before the purchase of the site, however straightforward the planning conditions may seem. Unless you are very sure that there are no complications, and you are very confident of getting approval, they should be re-consulted by your designer at the design stage, before the final drawings are prepared. If there are any concerns or controversial issues, more meetings may be appropriate. It is important to present ideas in person and talk through the drawings. Then sit back and listen carefully to what the planning officer says, and also how it is said. Try to get across the idea that you are going to deal honestly and fairly with them, and win their trust. If they are on your side, you will get a lot of useful advice and may avoid many problems later.

Do not try and hoodwink them or bluff them, or conceal your real intentions in the hope of tricking them into inadvertently agreeing to something. They know every trick in the book anyway, and at some point you are going to have to tell them what you intend to do. On no account get cross or threaten them in any way if you have irreconcilable differences. All that will happen is that they will cease to help you, whereas they are used to negotiating objectively and will not hold personal grudges just because you want to do something the planning authority will not allow – provided that you are polite.

Always get comments directly from a planning authority, in writing if possible. Be aware that any such comments cannot be relied upon, and the authority can ignore anything they have suggested informally when they make the actual decision.

Strategy and Compromise

If you have good reason to believe that your application will not be received with enthusiasm, work out carefully in advance with your architect what your strategy will be. Find some things that you would be prepared to offer as a compromise to get an approval. If you can be seen to be altering the design at the suggestion of the planning officer, it will play well with the neighbours, councillors or others who are pressing for more radical alterations. For example, you can offer to plant trees, or move windows, or even change the orientation of the house on the plot to reduce overlooking of neighbours, or put some of the first floor into the roof space to lower the ridge height – all of which will have a significant effect from beyond the plot boundary, without altering the design or layout.

Planners will only agree to compromises that can be expressly described and then enforced, so any promises that you make to do things will only count if they can either be put on a drawing or listed as a condition when approval is given. For example, 'We will plant some trees to screen a boundary' would need to be backed up with a plan, indicating the location and species. Even then, unless they get immediate Tree Preservation Orders on them, you could cut them down at a later date.

If, after all these tactics, you fail to win support for your proposal, you will have to be ready for a recommendation for refusal, but even then all is not lost. You can try to engender the support of the local community, preferably in writing.

One strategy sometimes used by professionals is to submit two separate applications for the same site. This is perfectly legal, and means that you can submit a controversial scheme alongside one that you do not like as much, but that is more likely to get approval. If the first one is rejected you will have the second in place and you will not lose the time that would have been needed for a re-submission. Additionally, you could go to

This house was built beyond the village boundary for development, but got approval after it was supported by most of the village.

appeal, where all argument would focus just on the difference between the two applications, rather than the proposal as a whole. If you feel that these kind of tactics may be necessary, seek expert advice as, once you take this path, you will have burned your bridges with the planners, who will see no reason to help you any further.

Problems with Planning Departments

Some planning authorities are better than others at handling their workload, and dealing with the public (as opposed to development professionals). Unfortunately, if local authorities are under-resourced they may decide to reduce the consultation service that they provide at the pre-application stage. There is no legal obligation on them to discuss prospective or submitted applications with the applicant to help them obtain an approval. Their duty is to properly consider the application, and then make a decision. If you are unlucky enough to encounter such an authority, you will have to make the application without any indication of its chances of success, and hope that you get the right decision and do not have to resubmit. The advice of a design professional familiar with the local planning concerns is essential in this situation.

Making a Planning Application

Having completed the initial consultation process, you should be ready to submit your application. The documentation has to be as accurate as possible, and everything should be carefully checked before submitting.

Types of Planning Application

An outline application can be nothing more than a set of completed forms and an Ordnance Survey map with a red line around the site. All you are asking for is approval in principle for a house to be built on the site. All the details, such as the access from the road and design of the building, may be made Reserved Matters. If a site already has outline planning approval, and you are not changing the principle established, you may either make an application for 'Approval of Reserved Matters' or put in a fresh application for full planning approval. Which you choose is down to individual circumstances.

Checklist for a Planning Application

- covering letters
- 4 sets of the completed application form
- 1 certificate of ownership
- 1 certificate of notification (if you do not yet own the site)
- 1 certificate of agricultural holding
- 4 copies of an Ordnance Survey location plan (with site boundary marked in red)
- 4 copies of the plans and elevations
- 4 copies of a site plan
- a cheque for the planning fee

If in a Conservation Area, typically also:

- 6, rather than 4, copies of the drawings
- design statement
- application for Conservation Area Consent if demolition is involved

The Drawings

The drawings will be the main focus of attention as the application is considered, and should be well presented and competently drawn. Poor presentation will harm the chances of approval, and inaccuracies may invalidate the approval unless the planners pick them up beforehand. However far you have progressed with the design, the drawings should contain as much information as necessary to obtain the approval, and no more. Everything that is on the approved drawings is part of the permission, and any changes require consent. This means that if you write 'natural stone' on the drawings because that is what you would like to use, but can't afford it when you come to build, you will need to seek permission not to use it. In fact, unless you are in an area of special control like a Conservation Area, the planners will normally put a condition on the approval that materials are to be approved at a later date.

> *All planning applications must be to a metric scale, even if you are more familiar with imperial measurements.*

Similarly, there is no point submitting drawings to 1:50 scale when 1:100 is usually perfectly acceptable. As the construction drawings are developed, it is normal for dimensions to change slightly. If the drawings are to a larger scale, the planners (and any objectors) can check what has been approved to a greater degree of accuracy, and this may help them to insist on an amendment being applied for. Just because you have diligently had a detailed levels survey prepared, you don't have to submit it as part of the application. The planners may ask for a few key dimensions to be written on the plans, especially if the site has a steep slope on it, but they don't need any more than this to properly consider the application.

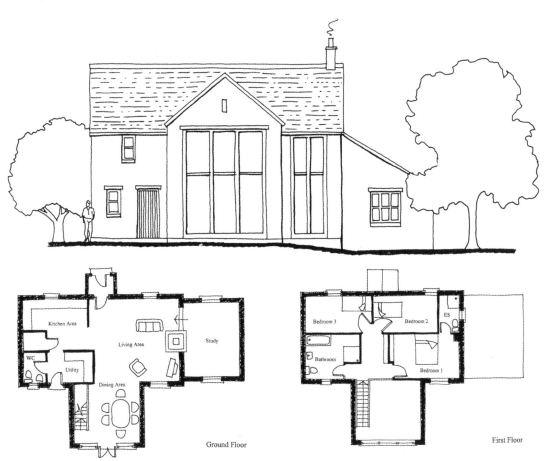

Some typical drawings, of the sort that would form part of a planning application.

A set of design drawings for a typical house will normally comprise two or three sheets of A3 paper, with 1:100-scale line drawings, each clearly marked with the name of the project and given a unique number. It may not look much, but if your architect has done a good job, a lot of the design will have been thought about in far greater detail than implied by the scale of the drawings. Background work to ensure that it can be built as indicated is essential, to avoid going back with a further application – caused by design modification resulting from problems with the construction detail, or in order to comply with Building Regulations.

Extra Information

Sometimes, especially if the building is prominent or in an area of special control, like a Conservation Area, the planners will request extra information. They may ask for computer models, photomontages or actual card models. In such areas, there is an increasing tendency to ask for 'design statements', that is written documents describing the approach to the design and how the surroundings have been taken into account. Unless it was obvious that this information would be needed from the very start, the architect may not have budgeted for it, so it may cost you extra to get it prepared – but it is a false economy to try to skimp on such things, because they will make the difference between success and failure.

This model gave a very good indication of the massing of the new house.

OS and accuracy

As part of the drawings, an Ordnance Survey plan must be included, to 1:1,250 scale. The area of the site must be outlined on the plan with red pen, and any areas next to the site that you own, or have an interest in, must be edged in blue pen. It is essential that this map is as accurate as reasonably possible. Usually the Land Registry map or deeds will show where it is, but if you have not yet purchased the site you should ensure that the vendor confirms where the boundary is. Apart from showing the planners clearly where the site is, this drawing also defines the area that is part of the application, and therefore excludes any surrounding land from it.

This computer simulation accurately shows how the finished building will look.

OS maps can be obtained through local authorities, or OS plan agencies. To photocopy an OS without permission is a breach of copyright rules, and, since your planning application is a matter of public record, it is unwise to ignore this restriction. The simplest way to get one is through your architect, who should have a licence to reproduce them, and can supply as many as are needed.

Filling in the Planning Form

The forms shown are typical examples of the kind of form that a council will require to be completed and submitted with the planning application. The information has to be correct and, to the best of your knowledge, accurate.

 If you have had discussions with a planning officer, make sure that they are named in the covering letter, and also refer to any correspondence that may have been sent. If you don't, and it is allocated to a different person who is unaware of them, your negotiations may not be taken into account.

Application for Planning Permission

Receipt No... Application No ....

Fee Paid £ .... Rec. ....

YOU ARE ADVISED TO READ THE ACCOMPANYING NOTES BEFORE COMPLETING THIS FORM.

Four copies of this form completed in BLOCK CAPITALS, the appropriate fee and completed Certificates under Article 7 must be submitted to the above address. Cheques should be crossed and made payable to Newtown District Council.

1. NAME AND ADDRESS OF APPLICANT	2. NAME AND ADDRESS OF Agent (if applicable)
MR AND MRS POTTER	JULIAN OWEN ASSOCIATES ARCHITECTS
PRIVET DRIVE	6 CUMBERLAND AVENUE
NEWTOWN	BEESTON, NOTTINGHAM
BORCETSHIRE	Post Code ... N69 4DH
Post Code ... HP1 1DH	Tel. No. ... 0115 922 9831
Tel. No. ... 01234 567890	Personal contact name ... JULAIN OWEN

3. FULL POSTAL ADDRESS OF THE APPLICATION SITE
   LAND ADJACENT TO 13 HILLTOP LANE, NEWTOWN, BORCETSHIRE

4. DESCRIPTION OF PROPOSED DEVELOPMENT
   NEW HOUSE

5. TYPE OF APPLICATION - PLEASE TICK APPROPRIATE BOX

☐ A Change of Use not involving building work

☑ B New Building Works (Which may also include a change of use) Alterations & Extensions.

   If box ticked, is application (i) FULL ☑
                                  (ii) OUTLINE ☐

☐ C Mining, Engineering or Other Operations

☐ D Approval of Reserved Matters
   Ref. of Outline permission.................................
   Date granted ....

☐ E Removal/Variation of a Condition
   Ref. of previous relevant permission
   ....
   Date granted ....

☐ F Renewal of Temporary Permission
   Ref. of previous temporary permission ....
   Date granted ....

If you ticked 5B(ii) please answer this question

6. OUTLINE APPLICATIONS

   A Please tick the items which are reserved for further consideration

   ☐ Siting   ☐ Design   ☐ Means of Access   ☐ External Appearance   ☐ Landscaping

7. SITE AREA
   Please state area of application site .... 500 ....Sq. m/hectares

Design and Planning
Getting Planning Permission

Application for Planning Permission

8. EXISTING USES

Please state existing or, if vacant, the last use(s) of the site or building ....RESIDENTIAL...

Please tick the appropriate box

9. DRAINAGE

A Disposal of surface water will be to: ☑ Mains sewer ☐ Soakaway ☐ Other

B Disposal of foul sewage will be to: - ☑ Mains sewer ☐ Cesspit ☐ Septic tank ☐ Other

10. TREES

Does the proposal involve the felling of any trees? ☐ Yes ☐ No

If the answer is YES, indicate the position on plan

11. ACCESS TO ROADS

Do you intend to form a new vehicular or pedestrian access to a public road, or alter an existing one?

☐ Yes ☑ No

12. RIGHTS OF WAY

Will the proposed development affect any public rights of way? ☑ Yes ☐ No

13. INDICATE GROSS FLOORSPACE FOR NON-RESIDENTIAL DEVELOPMENT

	Existing	Proposed
Industrial	............................m²	............................m²
Office	............................m²	............................m²
Retail	............................m²	............................m²
Warehousing	............................m²	............................m²
Ancillary Storage	............................m²	............................m²
Total gross floorspace	............................m²	............................m²

14. HAZARDOUS SUBSTANCES

Does the proposal involve the use or storage of a hazardous substance? ☐ Yes ☐ No

If YES state the type and quantity ....

15. Please complete

I attach plans

and I attach the completed Article 7 Certificate and the Agricultural Holdings Certificate

and I enclose the appropriate fee of £ ..220-00.............(see Fee List)

Signed..Applicant/Agent Date ..20-02-04......

Town and Country Planning (General Development Procedure) Order 1995

CERTIFICATE UNDER ARTICLE 7
PARTS ONE AND TWO OF THIS FORM MUST BE COMPLETED, SIGNED
AND DATED BY ALL APPLICANTS/APPELLANTS

PART 1 - LAND OWNERSHIP

For all certificates owner means a person having a freehold interest or a leasehold interest, the unexpired term of which was not less than 7 years. If the applicant is the owner of all the land, the subject of the application/appeal Certificate A is appropriate. In all other cases the applicant will need to serve the Notice under Article 6 attached on the persons(s) who was/were the owner(s) 21 days before the date of the accompanying application and complete Certificate B. If the owners of any of the land are unknown the applicant/appellant should obtain Certificate C or D from the Directorate of Planning and Development and complete and attach them to the application having complied with the procedure.

CERTIFICATE A

I certify that: -

On the 21 days before the date of the accompanying application nobody, except the applicant/~~appellant,~~ was the owner of any part of the land to which the application/appeal relates.

Signed.. Dated..........20-02-04..........

On behalf of*...........Mr & Mrs Potter...........

CERTIFICATE B

I have/The applicant/The appellant* has given the requisite notice to everyone else who, on the day 21 days before the date of the accompanying application/appeal, was the owner of any part of the land to which the application/appeal relates, as listed below.

Owner's name	Address at which notice was served	Date on which notice was served

Signed.. Dated..

On behalf of*... (Continue on separate page if necessary)

PART II - AGRICULTURAL HOLDINGS CERTIFICATE

None of the land to which the application relates is, or is part of, an agricultural holding

OR

I have/The applicant/The appellant* has given the requisite notice to every person other than my/him/her* self who, on the day 21 days before the date of the application/appeal, was a tenant of an agricultural holding on all or part of the land to which the application/appeal relates, as follows:

Tennants's name	Address at which notice was served	Date on which notice was served

Signed.. Dated..........20-02-04..........

* On behalf of............Mr & Mrs Potter............

* Delete as appropriate

Each item on the planning application form is explained below:

1. **Name and Address of Applicant.** You are the applicant, in a normal situation. You don't have to own the land to submit the application. Anyone can submit an application on someone else's land if they wish, as long as they tell them about it (see Planning Certificates Form).

2. **Name and Address of Agent.** If an architect or designer has prepared the drawings for you, it is usual for them to act as your agent. This means that any correspondence or queries go through them in the first instance.

3. **Full Postal Address of the Application Site.** Sometimes a piece of land may not have a proper postal address, in which case it must be described as accurately as possible. As long as there is an OS map indicating the exact boundaries, this will be acceptable.

4. **Description of Proposed Development.** The planners are interested in the use of whatever is being proposed.

5. **Type of Application.** Obviously a one-off house will be 'New Building Works', and you are probably asking for Full Permission.

6. **Outline Applications.** Generally, an approval of an outline application contains a list of Reserved Matters.

7. **Site Area.** This only has to be approximate, measured off the OS map. There are 10,000 square metres in a hectare.

8. **Existing Uses.** This will tell the planners if you are trying to change the use of the land or just intensify it; e.g. by building in a garden, the use of the land ,while not changing, will intensify from one house up to two.

9. **Drainage.** The Environment Agency may be consulted if there are watercourses near to the site, which may be affected by septic tanks, etc.

10. **Trees.** If any trees are to be felled, their location has to be plotted on the drawings.

11. **Access to Roads.** If you are creating a new drive and crossover with the pavement, the local highway authority will be consulted by the planners. If a trunk road is involved, the Highways Agency – a national body – will be informed. If these organisations refuse to agree to your proposed new access, the application will be refused, regardless of any other issues.

12. **Rights of Way.** If your development affects a right of way, get professional legal help before submitting the application.

13. **Indicate Gross Floorspace for Non-Residential Development.** For other kinds of development, the planning departments need more information to assess the impact of the proposal. Some local authorities send out separate forms to householders and self builders for this reason.

14. **Hazardous Substances.** This does not apply to private houses

15. **Signature.** A planning application must be complete and signed before it will be accepted and logged, and a cheque for the planning fee must also be sent. If there is anything missing, there will be a delay of one or two weeks, so that they can notify you and you can supply whatever has been missed.

Along with the actual application form, you also have to submit a certificate relating to the ownership and use of the land:

Part I – Land Ownership, Certificate A. You must be absolutely clear who owns all the land which forms the application, and only put your name on this certificate if you are quite certain that it is you.

Part I – Land Ownership, Certificate B. If the land belongs to someone else, you must send a notice to them when you submit, formally notifying them of what you are doing. This is to prevent unscrupulous people from getting an approval before buying land, without the owner knowing. Intentional failure to notify an owner, or a deliberate mis-statement about who owns the land, is a serious offence, and may also invalidate the planning application. If you don't know who the owner is, a notice has to be put in the local paper.

Part II Agricultural Holdings Certificate. This is to ensure that tenant farmers and others are notified of the application. Surprisingly, if a tenant is not farming the land and, for example, rents the property, there is no obligation to notify them, unless the lease is longer than seven years.

What Happens Once an Application is Submitted?

Acknowledgement

Assuming that the application has all the necessary drawings, documents and payment in place, an administration officer will log the application and allocate it to a planning officer.

Consultations

Once an officer has it on their desk, they will send out a series of letters to anyone that they think should know about it, inviting comments within 21 days.

Keeping in touch

If you have already had an pre-application meeting or contact with the planning department, refrain from making any follow-up calls before the end of the three or four weeks that the consultation takes. There will be nothing to discuss until comments are received from the parties being consulted.

Representations

Once you do contact the planning officer, if you then find there are unanticipated problems, arrange a meeting as soon as possible. Planning departments have targets for the time it should take to get a decision made, and they will want to either get a problem sorted out quickly, or reject the application very quickly if they don't believe that there is any possibility of a compromise.

Officer's report

Once an officer, in conjunction with the senior planner, has decided on a recommendation, a report will be prepared, usually recommending approval or rejection. In uncontroversial situations the decision may be delegated, which means that it is made by the planning staff rather than the council's planning committee, who simply 'rubber stamp' it.

Local councillors

In any situation where there have been several objections, or the approval may have important implications (e.g. if it is in a prominent location), the decision may be put to the Planning Committee for debate.

Planning Committee meetings

Planning Committee meetings are open to the public, and are often attended by interested parties, and journalists as observers The officers will make their case – in a written report sent out in advance, and with a verbal summary – before the matter is opened up for discussion. Some committees allow presentations from objectors and applicant. These usually have to be brutally short and, if you are not good at speaking in public, either get a professional like an architect to do it, or say nothing and confine yourself to lobbying councillors in private, in the hope that they will speak up on behalf of an approval.

Decision

As long as you know that the approval has been granted, you can count on the actual notice arriving in due course. It will take a week or so to go through the system, and will arrive at the office of your agent.

 The approval notice is an important document. Make sure that you get the original from your agent, not a copy.

Conditions

You may feel ready to relax about the planning approval now, but there is still a possible sting in the tail to be wary of, which is the list of conditions that are included as part of the notice, and are integral to the permission. Some of these are fairly routine, for example preventing work from starting on the house before the brick and tile types have been approved by the council. Others may be more onerous, can be added at the last minute, and may make the house more expensive, or less acceptable to you. An example may be an express requirement to accommodate more cars on the site, or, for someone who plans to work from home, a restriction on any ancillary business use. Other costly things that may be required are mining and contaminated land reports, or archaeological investigations. If you think a condition is unreasonable, or unenforceable, you can appeal against it in a similar way to a rejected application.

Appeals

If the application is refused, you may decide to resubmit an amended application – if it will help, and if you can accommodate the modifications – or lodge an appeal. If you are going to appeal, it is essential to get some professional advice, either from your architect or a planning consultant. Appeals are decided by a government-appointed inspector, who will be from outside the area, and can be in writing only – at a private hearing, or in public. The Planning Inspectorate publish an excellent booklet on how the appeal process works (available from your local planning office)

Summary

At the end of the planning process, you should have a piece of paper in your possession that gives you planning approval to build your house. After this point, if you have any minor changes, they can be agreed by the local authority as amendments to the application. If you have any major changes, for example significant alterations to the footprint or increases in the overall height, you will have to submit a fresh application. If you are lucky, the process from submission of the application to getting approval should take about eight weeks, if you have serious problems, it could take twice as long.

1. Obtain all existing planning documents from the vendor, and confirm the ownership boundary.
2. Check for special controls in the area, e.g. Conservation Area.
3. Hold a preliminary meeting with the planning officer.

4. Consult any interested parties, e.g. highways department, Parish Council.

5. Obtain the planning application forms.

6. Finalise the design.

7. Consult the neighbours.

8. Submit the application and pay the fee.

9. Check with the planning officer 3–4 weeks after submission.

10. Meet the planning officer and discuss any amendments, if necessary.

11. Receive the decision notice.

Building Regulations and Tenders

Once the planning application has been submitted and approved, you are ready to start preparing the information that will describe how the building is to be built. The more that is decided on and fully described before you start on site, the easier it will be to build, and the less likely you are to get into a cash-flow problem. You need to get the approval of the basic house construction from the local authority building control officer, and to present the information to all the suppliers, manufacturers and builders that you will be dealing with, in as comprehensive and clear a way as possible. You also need to select the team who will help you to construct the house, and be sure that they have given you accurate prices.

Summary of This Stage:

- Submitting a Building Regulations Application
- Preparing a Tender Package
- Finding Building Contractors
- Getting a Price for the Work

Submitting a Building Regulations Application

Once you have both acquired your site and obtained planning permission, the next key task is to obtain approval under the Building Regulations. Although the approval is usually given by the same department of the local authority, this is a separate exercise from obtaining planning permission. Obtaining planning approval does not imply that a design will get Building Regulations approval, and vice versa. If you have been using a professional to prepare your plans, they will be very familiar with the current regulations and will ensure that your planning drawings can also comply with the regulations.

Table 12: Getting Building Regulations Approval						
Planning approval received	Prepare Building Regulations documents	Submit Building Regulations application	building control officer sends a letter with queries	Building control officer checks application	Architect provides answers to queries	Full plans approval granted
	4 – 6 weeks		3 weeks		2 weeks	

What are the Building Regulations?

The Building Regulations have been created to ensure that all significant building work complies with some minimum standards of construction. This protects the people who are to use a building by, for example, checking that the structure is sound. But they also ensure that the interests of the general community are served – enforcing, for instance, the need for the burning of fossil fuels to be kept to a minimum. The main regulations, passed by parliament, state that a building must comply with these requirements, and guidance on how this might be achieved is given in a set of booklets called 'Approved Documents' (see section below).

The Approved Documents are regularly updated, which means that designers and builders have to make sure that they keep abreast of changes. If you can find other ways of complying with the law, which could be summed up as 'it should be designed and built properly', you do not necessarily have to follow the examples illustrated in the Approved Documents.

Getting Building Regulations approval is quite different to the highly subjective planning-approval process. Whether or not a building complies is here mostly a matter of fact, rather than opinion. Building control officers are usually very pragmatic people, and will agree to changes and improvements on site if necessary.

The ultimate responsibility for compliance with the regulations is on the developer, i.e. you. It can be delegated to a main contractor or site manager, but the buck stops with the self builder.

 Make sure that it is written into your contract with a builder that it is their responsibility to liaise with building control on site and ensure that the regulations are complied with.

Notice and Full Plans

There are two ways of getting approval under the regulations, and of completing the building of a house. The safest procedure involves two stages. Drawings and specifications describing the basic construction of the building are prepared, and submitted with a fee. The application is for 'Full Plans Approval'. After about three weeks a building control officer writes to whoever has submitted the plans, asking for any amendments or extra information. Once this is provided satisfactorily, Full Plans Approval is granted – in the form of an approval notice, along with a set of plans stamped 'Approved'. Quite often, approval will be conditional on further information which is not currently available being provided – for example, roof-truss calculations which will only be provided by a supplier once an order is placed, long after construction has started.

The approval usually takes between five and eight weeks to come through after submission, and you can then start work on site after giving a couple of days' notice. You can now start work fairly confident that the house will comply with all the major requirements of the regulations, and you have some drawings that can be used as a basis for its construction.

 Building Regulations drawings are not sufficient to get accurate tenders from contractors to build the whole house – only the basic structure and construction are covered.

Assuming the drawings and specifications are followed, and any changes are agreed with the building control officer beforehand, you can maintain this confidence throughout the project. The building control officer will make periodic inspections at key points in the build programme. On completion, you will get a certificate that states that the house has been built to the regulations, something that will be essential if you intend to sell the property later. A fee is paid – about 25 per cent of the total when the plans are submitted, with the balance being paid once work starts.

If a project is very simple and straightforward, like the porch to a house, or if it involves a standard design that has been approved before, it is possible to use the Building Notice procedure. A simple form is completed 48 hours before work starts, along with a fee. No detailed drawings or specifications are required. This route is not suitable for most self-build projects for a number of reasons. If anything is built that does not comply with the regulations, it may not be noticed until later on, requiring work to be taken down and rebuilt. You, or your builder, will carry the risk of delay and extra cost if this happens. If you want an architect to certify, you will struggle to find one who is prepared to shoulder the risk of inspecting a site without a set of Building Regulations drawings to work from. The fee to serve a Building Notice is the same as for the Full Plans Approval route but, instead of being paid in two stages, it is all due when the notice is sent.

Types of Building Control Service

At one time, all Building Regulations applications were only dealt with by the local authority responsible for the area where the building work was being carried out. The current system allows private companies, using 'Approved Inspectors', and other local authorities to provide a building control service. So, any organisations which have suitable expertise, staff and insurance cover can qualify to provide it. A good example of this is the National House Building Council (NHBC), which combines an inspection service with its other certification services. Most local authorities offer a plans approval service for projects outside their area, leaving the inspection stage to others. The benefits of this arrangement are mainly to large developers, builders and architects, who may form a mutually beneficial relationship with one of their local authorities.

For one-off developers like self builders, it is generally better to make use of whichever local authority covers the area in which you are building. The local officers are a very useful source of information at an early stage, with an intimate knowledge of things like ground conditions. Building control officers have always been amongst the most helpful officials in the building industry, and they are keener than ever to help now that they have competition.

England and Wales v Scotland

The procedure covered in this book mainly relates to the Building Regulations as they apply in England and Wales. Scotland has a few differences. North of the Border, work cannot start until a Building Warrant has been issued (you can start before plans approval has been granted in England and Wales, if you wish). The Scots also base the size of the fee on the construction cost, whereas in England and Wales, unless the house is very large, the fee is a flat rate for a single dwelling. In Scotland, a house cannot be occupied unless a Habitation Certificate has been issued at the end of the project. In Northern Ireland the rules are very similar to those in England and Wales.

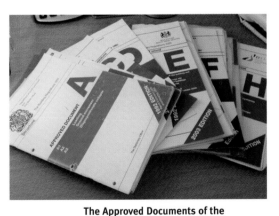

The Approved Documents of the Building Regulations.

Approved Documents (ADs)

At the centre of the Building Regulations approval process is a set of documents, lettered from A to N (in 2004), that methodically go through each aspect of building construction and give detailed advice on how to meet the requirements. Copies can be ordered from most bookshops, and anyone who is contemplating being directly involved in the building work should ensure that they have a set before starting.

Even a well-prepared set of plans will not cover every regulation that applies. Many of the regulations are assumed to apply, or may be included using phrases such as 'drains to be laid in accordance with Approved Document H of the Building Regulations'. The purpose of the Full Plans Approval is to identify compliance of the major aspects of the construction, not to list every last paragraph from the Approved Documents. Consequently, no-one should work on your project unless they have a basic knowledge of the Approved Documents. Much of the guidance covers non-domestic buildings and will be irrelevant to you, but all of the ADs have something in them that affects the way that houses are planned and built.

One strange anomaly is that most of the Building Regulations do not apply to the construction of external works, beyond the immediate area of the house.

Some of the Approved Documents of the Building Regulations

A. Structure

B. Fire Safety

C. Site Preparation and Resistance to Moisture

D. Toxic Substances

E. Resistance to the Passage of Sound

F. Ventilation

G. Hygiene

H. Drainage and Waste Disposal

J. Combustion Appliances and Fuel Storage Systems

K. Protection From Falling, Collision and Impact

L. Conservation of Fuel and Power

M. Access and Facilities for Disabled People

N. Glazing – Safety in relation to Impact, Opening and Cleaning

P. Electrical safety (from Jan 2005)

Making a Building Regulations Application

A Full Plans Building Regulations application should include:

- a covering letter
- a completed application form
- 2 copies of the location plan (usually the same one as used for the planning application)
- 2 sets of drawings, including plans, elevations and sections at 1:50 scale
- 2 sets of specifications, which may be in the form of a separate document or written on the drawings
- 2 sets of structural calculations
- a cheque for the Full Plans Approval application fee (will vary between authorities)

Drawings and Specifications

If you are using an architect to prepare a tender package as well as to obtain Building Regulations approval, the same set of drawings and specifications may be used for both. If you have asked for 'Building Regulations only' this is probably what you will get – just enough information to get Full Plans Approval and no more. These drawings do not need to be exhaustive, and will not tackle any of the detailed construction problems, which will have to be sorted out on site if not worked out beforehand. Usually 1:50 scale is acceptable, even for a section through the building, which does not really tell you much about the construction, other than the broad principles – but this is all the building control officer is looking for at this stage.

Some local authorities insist on an Ordnance Survey location plan before they will log a Full Plans application, on the grounds that they need the property accurately identified. However, this is not a strict requirement in the same way as for a planning application. Hopefully, given the correct address, a building control officer is sufficiently experienced to spot a house under construction.

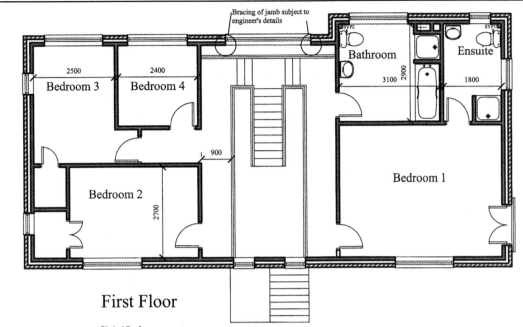

Bracing of jamb subject to engineer's details

2500	2400
Bedroom 3	Bedroom 4

Bathroom 3100 2900

Ensuite 1800

900

Bedroom 2 2700

Bedroom 1

SVP2 SVP1

First Floor

Pitched Roof
Trussed rafter roof structure, to manufacturer's design. Attic trusses, @ 600mm intervals, bearing onto 50 x 100mm.
Bracing to be 100 x 25mm sw, 'chevron' pattern in plan, with continuous longitudinal ridge brace, all in accordance with Appendix 7.2-E of Volume 2 of NHBC standards, BS 5268:Part 3 and Building Regulations. Fix bracing and binders to every rafter, strut or tie with not less than two 75 x 3.35mm galvanised round wire nails.
Clay pantiles, from the Sandtoft 'County Pantile' range. Lap and gauge to manufacturer's instructions on 25 x 38mm Type A sw battens, on BS 747 type 1F roofing felt or similar.
Insulation to ceiling to be provided by 200mm Rockwool glass fibre quilt or equivalent, with wpb plywood board fixed between rafters over wallplate to ensure flow of air.

Foundations
600mm concrete trench fill foundations, founded at or below the level of the existing building - assume 1000mm - subject to engineer's comments and design (see engineer's report dated 02.08.99 in appendix) and building control officer's approval, with C385 fabric in accordance with engineer's recommendations.

Floor Construction
Ground Floor. 150mm suspended precast concrete pot and beam floor, to manufacturer's design, with 50mm insulation and 75mm screed reinforced with D49 mesh, and in accordance with manufacturer's details (see manufacturer's details). NOTE: floor insulation and construction to be checked once underfloor heating system has been selected and design, and revised if necessary.
Insulation to have a 25mm upstand to the perimeter walls.
First Floor construction to be 150mm precast concrete pot and beam floor, all to manufacturer's recommendations, with 75mm screed, reinforced with D49 mesh. Bearing onto internal block walls and inner leaf of external walls.
First Floor to be cantilevered to form gallery inaccordance with engineer's details and mnaufacturer's design.
Ceilings to be lined with 9.5mm plasterboard with joints covered with jute scrim, and skim coat. Noggins to all edges. (12.5mm plasterboard to ground floor ceilings).

Walls
External wall construction to consist of 102mm Ibstock Mellow Red bricks (FL quality). 100mm cavity fill in sulation, with Owens Corning mineral wool cavity wall batts or equivalent. 100mm Topblock 'Toplite' blockwork. All to achieve min u-value of 0.45 W/sqmK.
13mm two coat plaster to internal surface of blockwork.
Stainless steel vertical twist wall ties to BS 1243:1978 @ 750mm horizontal spacing and 450mm vertical spacing, at 300mm vertical intervals, and within 225mm of openings.
Cavity filled with weak mix concrete below ground level.
Wall dpc to be at min 150mm height above external ground level.
Weepholes at 900mm intervals immediately above ground level and over openings.
Reinforced precast concrete lintels over openings to internal blockwork walls.
Fit Catnic CN14 steel lintel with integral cavity tray or equivalent over flat window openings, with soldier course over.
Fit pc concrete lintel, with brick arch in front for arched head openings, all in accordance with the drawings.
Window cills to be precast stone by proprietary manufacturer.
Precast stone coping to the parapets.

Fires
Living Room to have a ventilation openings in the form of airbricks with a total free area of at least 50% of the appliance throat opening area, - as defined in BS 8303: 1986 *Code of Practice for installation of domestic heating and cooking appliances burning solid mineral fuels*. Appliance to be enclosed, details to be confirmed.
Boiler to be oil fired unvented mains pressured condensing boiler, installed by a competent person as defined under the Building Regulations. Installer's and manufacturer's certificates to be provided.

Disabled Access
Level approach to have gradient not steeper than 1 in 20, with firm and even and min width of 900mm.
Accessible threshold at the entrance to be provided (in accordance with drawing in the appendix).
External front door providing to have a minimum clear opening width of 775mm.

Heating and Hot & Cold Water
Hot water supply to whbs, sinks, bath and showers from new oil fired central heating and hot water system.
Radiators generally below window cills, tbc by clients.
Fit adjustable thermostatic valves to all new radiators except in Bathroom.
Cold water to appliances as required.
All pipe runs to be concealed in floor or ceiling voids where possible.

Electrical Work
Mechanical extract to WC, Bathroom and Kitchen as described earlier, wired into lighting circuit, including external grille and anti backdraught flaps.
Provide central 100W light bulbs with pull cord light switches, general lighting scheme and special fittings tbc by client.
All new wiring to be concealed in floor or ceiling voids where possible. Chased into wall in new building, concealed in surface mounted trunking elsewhere.
All work to be in accordance with current IEE regulations.

Floor and Wall finishes
Fit glazed ceramic tiles to bathrooms etc, and to window cill s in bathrooms, Utility and Kitchen, tbc by clients.
Paint all new woodwork with primer and two no coats gloss paint.

Drawings like this, often with the specifications written on, are typical of the kind required for a Building Regulations application.

Many local authorities check Building Regulations drawings against the drawings that have received planning approval, and will pick up any changes that need further consideration by the planning process. But there is no obligation for them to do this, so someone on your team should review any alterations to ensure that there are no problems.

Structural Calculations

Approved Document A is about making sure that the building will stay up, and will comfortably bear the loads and stresses that are put upon the structure. To demonstrate this, calculations will have to be prepared, and the usual person to do this is the structural engineer. These calculations will be related to things such as adequacy of the foundations for a given type of soil, the size of beams, and the stability of walls. Once they have been submitted, they are checked by another engineer, who may or may not be employed directly by the local authority.

Filling in the Form

The application form is mercifully short, and only requires the most basic information about the project. The questions to pay special attention to are:

Item 5. You should always agree to conditional approval. The alternative is that the application will be refused unless everything of concern has been approved, even though the information may not be available because it is going to be provided later. However, it is very important that this information is submitted and approved before the relevant work is carried out.

Item 6. Likewise, it is sensible to agree to an extension of time to the prescribed period. Like their planning colleagues, building control officers are under pressure to deal with applications promptly, so if they run out of time and you won't agree to extend it, they will issue a rejection notice.

Item 7. A house is not covered by most of the fire regulations.

Item 8. It is essential that a Completion Certificate is asked for at this point. If it not, there will be no obligation for one to be issued, and it is a vital document if the house is to be sold on.

Item 16. If the house is larger than the average, typically over 300 sq m, the fee will be calculated in a different way to that for houses below this size.

Unlike a planning application, you have to pay VAT on the Building Regulations fee – make sure that, when you write the cheque, it has been added on.

Working With Building Control Officers

Unless a proposal involves the simplest of structures, the building control officer will usually have some questions, or require extra information, after a full plans application has been submitted, and before it is approved. Because there is no prescribed level of information, similar applications to different local authorities, or even different officers within the same authority, will elicit a different set of queries. If there is a good working relationship between the designer and the building control officer, this checking process can be invaluable to both sides, and helps to ensure that any areas which may be a potential problem are picked up and dealt with at an early stage. Likewise, a competent officer inspecting a site provides an extra pair of eyes, working on your behalf.

Building Regulations Full Plans Application

Receipt No.. Application No ....

Fee Paid £ .... Rec. ....

Notice of intention to erect, extend, or alter a building, execute works or install fittings or make a material change of use of an existing building.

I/~~We~~ hereby give notice of intention to carry out the work set out herein in accordance with the accompanying plans.

Signed.. Date ....21-07-04............

---

1. NAME AND ADDRESS OF APPLICANT
MR AND MRS POTTER

PRIVET DRIVE

NEWTOWN

BORCETSHIRE

Post Code ......HP1 1DH......

Tel. No. ......01234 567890......

2. NAME AND ADDRESS OF Agent (if applicable)
JULIAN OWEN ASSOCIATES ARCHITECTS

6 CUMBERLAND AVENUE

BEESTON, NOTTINGHAM

Post Code ......N69 4DH......

Tel. No. ......0115 922 9831......

Personal contact name ......JULAIN OWEN......

---

3. FULL POSTAL ADDRESS OF THE APPLICATION SITE
LAND ADJACENT TO 13 HILLTOP LANE, NEWTOWN, BORCETSHIRE

---

4. DESCRIPTION OF PROPOSED DEVELOPMENT
NEW HOUSE

---

5. CONDITIONS Do you consent to the plans being passed subject to conditions where appropriate? — YES/~~NO~~

6. EXTENSION OF TIME If it is not possible to give a determination within the prescribed period do you consent to an extension of time? — YES/~~NO~~

7. Is the building to be put to a Designated Use for the purpose of the Fire Precautions Act? — ~~YES~~/NO

8. Do you wish to receive a Completion Certificate on completion of the work? — YES/~~NO~~

9. Is a new vehicular crossing over the footway required? — YES/~~NO~~

10. Means of water supply — MAINS

11. Details and dates of any additions made to the property since 1948 (this includes garage, conservatory, etc.) — N/A

12. State whether building is private, Council or ex Council — PRIVATE

13. Amount of fee enclosed herewith — £ 176-25

14. Fee payable for inspection of work — £ 205-63

15. Estimated total cost of work — £ 180,000

16. Floor area of proposal Sq. m — 190

This form must be accompanied by two sets of plans and the appropriate fee.
Where Part B (Fire Safety) applies a further two sets of plans are required.

Building Regulations and Tenders

Submitting a Building Regulations Application

Site Inspections

Two days before the work starts on site, the building control officer must be informed, and the inspection fee paid (or the Notice fee, if you are courageous enough to do it that way). There will then be a series of inspections at those points in the building programme that are most critical, each of which officially requires at least one day's notice. Building control officers generally start work early and deal with office administration duties until around 10.00 a.m., after which they will set off to carry out their inspections. Provided a builder can telephone before this time, a site meeting can usually be set up for the same day, thus avoiding having builders standing around waiting for a visit before they can carry on with their work.

The building control officer's brief is to check that the Building Regulations are being complied with – not to provide a site inspection service to you, or to monitor the progress of the builder. A particularly helpful officer will make informal comments, off the record, but most do not have the time to get involved with quality-control issues, or want the aggravation. For example, if a brick wall has been built well enough to stand up, it is not their concern if it does not look good, or that it is patchy because the pallets of brickwork have not been properly mixed after delivery. Likewise, if the specification or design has been changed, as long as it still complies you should not expect a building control officer to point this out. It is not part of their job.

Building Control Inspection Stages

- commencement (2 days' notice)
- foundation trenches dug, but not filled
- foundation trenches filled with concrete
- subfloor ready, concrete slab about to be laid
- damp-proof course level reached
- drains – laid, but not backfilled
- drains testing
- occupation (if not yet compete)
- completion (2 days' notice)
- certificate issued
- all the above require one day's notice, except where stated otherwise

What Can Go Wrong?

If you make a Full Plans application, the likelihood of something going wrong is greatly reduced, and the problems are not usually complex. Occasionally, something proposed – or even built – does not meet with the approval of the building control officer.

Failure at Full Plans stage

If something is wrong on the plans, the list of queries issued halfway through the approval process will pick it up, and it can probably be easily corrected. That is assuming that it is not something fundamental to the design, preventing the site from being used at all (which is very rare), or that the necessary changes do not affect the planning approval. An example of the former is a discretionary requirement that says that a fire engine must not have to reverse away from a house for more than 20 m, which in practice means that if your site is too small to accommodate a fire engine's turning circle and is accessed by a narrow track longer than this distance, the Building Regulations requirements could prevent the house from being built. An example of the latter is when the regulations state that a first-floor bedroom must have an opening window with a sill low enough to climb out if there is a fire, but this would look out over the neighbours' garden – something that the planner would not allow.

A rejection of a Full Plans application is not as bad as it sounds, since if you resubmit with amendments straight away, most of the checking will have already been done and the approval can come through in a matter of days.

Failure to comply on site

If you or your contractor builds something that does not follow the approved drawings and specifications, or that was not covered by them, and the building control officer decides that it is contrary to the Building Regulations, your only realistic option is to demolish it and rebuild. The building control officer has considerable powers to halt and condemn work if you try to ignore any direction to correct a contravention. There is an appeals process, in which you ask for the government to decide if you are right, or that the rules should be relaxed in your case. In the context of building a private house, you would have to be pretty desperate to try this, since it will result in extra cost and delay to the programme.

Speeding up the Process

The ideal progression is to wait for planning approval, then have a Building Regulations package prepared, then a tender package, and then appoint a contractor, who starts work after Building Regulations approval. This all takes time, but is the safest way to proceed and will greatly reduce the risks. But, if there is an unavoidable rush, several things can be done to get on to site more quickly. You can ask your designer to start work on the Building Regulations before planning approval is granted. The disadvantage of this is that any changes that result from the input of the planning system will require the more-detailed Building Regulations drawings to be amended, at extra cost. Legally, you cannot start work before you have planning approval.

Another way to save time is to start on site immediately after the application for full plans has been lodged, which is fine provided you are totally confident that any work affected by the first few weeks of building will definitely comply. You are unlikely to get your designer or builder to guarantee this, however, because the consequences of being wrong can be very expensive – and it will be your risk. But this is still a better option than the high-risk route of serving a Building Notice, without any drawings at all, because the checking process will eventually catch up with the building work, and you will get warning of any problems only at that point.

A compromise is to wait until the initial queries come back before starting to build, which will at least indicate the areas that are questionable. If none of the queries involves the early stages of construction, you will know it is safe to start digging. Unfortunately, it is not unusual for a letter from Building Control to state that checking of structural calculations by the local authority is still under way and that any questions regarding these may come later. There would be an obvious risk in carrying out any work covered by the structural calculations, before approval is in place.

Summary

To get approval under the Building Regulations, whoever designs and builds your house has to comply with the Approved Documents, and nothing more. Anything not in them does not need to get approval. Aspects of the work like decorations, fittings and fixtures, and most of the electrical work, are of no direct interest to the building control officer. Consequently, do not expect a Building Regulations package to be sufficient on its own to fully describe the building that is going to be built. A lot more decisions have to be made – by a designer producing a proper tender package, by you, by the contractor or subcontractor, or by the worker on site wielding a trowel.

Preparing a Tender Package

Having jumped the bureaucratic hurdles and got your Full Plans application to the building control officer, you may think that the majority of the design work is now complete. However, as already mentioned, the drawings and specification that will keep a building control officer happy are not usually detailed enough for a contractor to either price from, or construct a whole building. What you do next will partly depend on your chosen construction route. But all the details of the construction have to be worked out by someone, ideally before the day that the labourers and tradesmen arrive on site to start building. How your project proceeds from this point, and how much information you need to add, over and above the Building Regulations package, depends on how you intend to build. The table below shows some of the implications for the typical build routes.

The section that follows is designed to help those who are preparing to get tenders from contractors for the whole project, but much of the information also applies to self managers and those who are going to take the DIY route.

Table 13: How Your Choice of Building Method Affects Your Project				
	Main Contractor Design-Build	Main Contractor Build Only	Managed Subcontractors	DIY Self Build
Price	Fixed at planning stage.	Fixed at tender stage.	Updated as building proceeds.	Updated as building proceeds.
Quality	Completely under contractor's control.	Strictly controlled by you usually through an architect.	Controlled by project manager or you day-to-day.	Controlled by you day-to-day.
Drawings and Specification required	Drawings by builder, outline specifications only, no detailed drawings.	Full working drawings and specifications , all worked out before tenders invited.	Either Building Regulations drawings only, or tender package.	Usually Building Regulations drawings only, produced by an architect.
Site Management	Contractor	Contractor	You, or your project manager.	You
Choice of Materials	Mostly chosen by contractor.	Mostly chosen by you, usually with an architect advising	You, helped by each subcontractor.	You
Insurances	Contractor	Contractor	You	You
Health & Safety Responsibility	Contractor	Contractor	You, or your project manager	You
Payment	At agreed stages	At agreed stages	At stages, or at end of each week	N/A
Certification	Provided by builder	By an architect employed by you, or by project warranty-provider	By architect employed by you, or by project warranty-provider	By architect employed by you, or by project warranty-provider
Programme	Controlled by contractor	Controlled by contractor, usually monitored by an architect	Controlled by you, or your project manager	Controlled by you and your family

What is a Tender Package?

The objective for anyone preparing a tender package is to leave as little to doubt as is reasonably possible. If a decision can be made before you invite builders to price, they are likely to put a lower price on it than if you ask them after they know that they are the lowest tenderer, and much lower than if you ask them when they are already on site. It is also essential to make the drawings and specifications as thorough and unambiguous as possible. If something is not referred to, the contractor may not price it and it will become an 'extra' once you are on site and ask for it. If the description is ambiguous as to who will provide something, then contractors will probably assume it will not be them when they are pricing.

It follows from this that if you are going to ask for tenders for something as complex as a house designed to your own individual requirements, trying to save money by not having a detailed tender package can be a false economy. If you use only Building Regulations drawings, or pay the minimum to get a basic specification, you may save a few thousand pounds initially. But this course of action could easily cost many times that amount later on. Even with a detailed package of information, tender prices often vary by tens of thousands of pounds, because a contractor's calculations are based on a mix of how busy they are, keenness to get the job, how easy it is to get the right trades, and more straightforward factors such as the distance from their office and how many other projects they have in the pipeline.

Inadequate drawings and specifications are a good way to get lumbered with the worst builders, at a premium price. A decent builder, when pricing, will allow for all the things that you have missed, and consequently appear to be expensive. A crafty one will omit everything they can from the tender price, then hit you with inflated prices for extras once work has started.

Sources of Information

A typical tender package, as produced by an architect, should be the result of several weeks of hard work and collaboration with you. Once you start to look at all the detailed things that go into a building, which need to be decided upon individually by you, it is surprising how much there is to be dealt with and researched. Your professional advisors can obviously help you with this task by suggesting alternatives and new ideas, but you should also have been doing your own investigations. If you are organised, you will already have a stack of product literature, magazine excerpts, notes and photos. If the timing is right, this is a good point to visit one of the exhibitions that are held across the country, and pay closer attention to the advertisements and features in the magazines. The exhibitions are useful because you will be able to talk directly to the manufacturers and suppliers of products, and collect useful information on their prices and availability.

If you are going to an exhibition to get detailed information, go during the week rather than the weekend, ideally the first day of the show, and as early as possible. At busy times, people on the stands will not be available for long discussions. Make sure you take spare sets of plans to leave behind if you want quotations.

What Goes into a Detailed Tender Package?

A comprehensive tender package will be as complete a description as you and your architect can manage. There will inevitably be some details that you are not able to decide upon, and other things that will be unknown, such as the ground conditions. If you cannot or do not want to decide on something, it is alright to leave it out – provided you make this clear in the documents, and then adjust your budget to allow for it going into the cost later. Because even the most virtuous contractors will tend to price items added on site a bit higher, you should at least try to describe the labour element and get that included at the start. For example, you can specify that a wash basin is to be supplied by 'others', but fitted by the contractor. This will allow you to shop for it later on, when you can actually see what the bathroom looks like, buy it yourself, and have it fitted by the contractor.

If you are going to purchase anything separately, ask the contractors to quote for its supply or suggest a similar product first. It may be cheaper if they can get a good discount.

It is beyond the scope of this book to advise on the detailed design and construction of a house, but a typical selection of things that need to be described in a detailed specification is listed in the checklist below. It is important that the final decisions on these aspects of the house are made by you and your family, rather than by anyone else. Apart from the first section, almost all of the items listed have implications for your budget, and it is sensible to have an idea of the cost involved – at least for the supply of the materials if not the labour element, which is difficult to predict. If you are a typical client, you will at this point specify more than your budget can afford, and you will have to trim down your expectations when you get firm prices later on.

Some Typical Items to be Included in a Detailed Specification

General conditions

- rate of liquidated damages
- timing of payments
- retention
- working hours
- who co-ordinates services

Excavations

- can any waste spoil be disposed of on site?
- topsoil to be retained and reused on site?

Floors

- precast concrete upper floor, or timber joists?
- chipboard or solid concrete finish?
- underfloor heating required?

Walls

- brick colour, texture, surface and pointing style
- high level of insulation, or minimum required by Building Regs?
- type of sills and heads, any specialist brickwork, e.g. dentil courses
- any fireplaces – if yes, inglenook or standard – what kind of fire surround?

Pitched Roof

- trussed rafters or open roof?
- tile material, e.g. clay or concrete?

- tile colour; and type, e.g. plain or interlocking?
- high level of insulation, or minimum required by Building Regs?
- valleys formed from lead or plastic?
- concealed soil stack and mechanical ventilation outlets through roof?

Flat Roof

- standard construction or specialist, such as single-ply or lead?

Internal Doors

- construction, e.g. flush; pressed fibreboard; timber mortice, tenon and wedged?
- finish, e.g. self-finished, painted, stained or varnished?
- ironmongery type, e.g. brushed aluminium, brass finish, plastic?
- ironmongery type, e.g. lever handles, knobs?
- locks, e.g. mortice locks, bolts?

External Doors and Windows

- construction, e.g. upvc, softwood, hardwood?
- glazing, e.g. safety glass, triple glazing, argon-filled units?
- style, e.g. plain casements, cottage style, Georgian, real or fake leaded lights?
- ironmongery finish; and type, e.g. friction stays, letterbox?

- locks, e.g. rim latches, mortice locks, hinge bolts?
- garage door type, style and mechanism

Joinery

- staircase construction, e.g. timber or concrete?
- staircase joinery style – handrails, bannisters and newel posts
- who fits the kitchen, and do they do other things, e.g. lighting and tiling?
- fitted cupboards
- airing cupboard
- skirtings, trims and architraves

Sanitary Goods

- manufacturer and model number
- taps, e.g. chrome, brass finish; monoblock, thermostatic mixer?
- WC suite lid type
- vanity units

Heating System

- fuel source, e.g. gas, oil, electricity?
- boiler type, e.g. combination, mains-pressured, condensing?
- heating method, e.g. underfloor, radiators, air-blown, perimeter heating (in a kitchen)?

Electrical Services

- numbers of sockets, lights, and switches for each room, located on a plan if possible
- types of fitting, e.g. security lights, wall-mounted, pendants, bulkhead fittings?
- special circuits, e.g. electric cooker
- other wiring, e.g. computer networking cable, TV sockets, security system?

Surface Finishes

- walls – papered or painted?
- ceiling – any textured finishes?
- floor, e.g. quarry tiles, laminated, carpeted?
- tiling – where and to what extent?

External Works

- areas of hardstanding/driveway
- finish to driveway, e.g. gravel, concrete blocks?
- type and location of walls and fences
- gate locations and types
- any external features, e.g. pillar light, outside taps?
- ponds and water features

Budget Check

As ever, you should at least have an eye on your budget, and be in a continuing discussion with your architect as to whether it is prudent to include any of the more expensive items in your specification. You should allow a contingency on top of your budget for unexpected items that may crop up on site, or last minute additions that you may wish to make. At the start of the construction stage, this should be a minimum of 5 per cent of the tender price. Some people suggest that you should state a contingency sum in the tender documents. This is often done on commercial projects, where budgets are fixed by managers and such figures need to be included for accounting reasons. In your case, there is no need to tell the contractors that you have contingencies – in fact if you can convince then that you are breaking the bank to pay for it and that even a little extra cost will be painful, it may help persuade them to keep their extras at a realistic level.

For similar reasons, you should not give the contractor the opportunity to include in their tendered price what are called 'prime cost sums' and 'provisional sums'. Both of these are sometimes included in a tender by a contractor, to avoid fixing the price. They are suggested costs for some items of the work, which can be revised as work progresses (often upwards). If the work can be fully described and the contractors are competent, it should be possible for them to quote a fixed price.

Finding Building Contractors

As you are having your design and tender package prepared, you can also start to tackle one of the most important decisions in the whole project: finding the contractors who will go on your tender list, and choosing which will build your home. You need an absolute minimum of three prices to be tendered, preferably more. A building contractor's decision on which projects they will tender for is influenced by their workload, which can change overnight when they win a contract. As a result, it is not unusual for a contractor to agree to tender one day, and change their mind the next. They may let you know they have changed their mind and send back the documents, but may either not bother to submit a price, or inflate their tender to an unrealistically high figure so that if by some accident they do get the job, it will have a very big profit margin to compensate for the extra trouble. So a reasonable number of contractors to approach is five or possibly six, allowing for one or two to drop out along the way, or to overprice. If you really must go to more, bear in mind that there will be extra costs to you in producing further copies of the tender package.

If you ask for lots of tenders, don't be surprised if many drop out – it is a lot of work for building contractors to calculate a price accurately, and they want a reasonable chance of winning. They can find out who else is pricing from shared suppliers or subcontractors.

How to Find Builders

Unlike most of the professions, builders are not licensed, which means that anyone with a mobile phone and a truck can advertise themselves as one. Unemployed DIY enthusiasts, firemen, funeral directors and software designers have all done just this, with mixed results. Much like choosing your professional advisors, the strategy is to draw up a list of apparently likely firms and whittle it down by a checking procedure. Part of the problem is that contractors who are good at what they do, don't have to advertise – they get most of their work through personal recommendation. The problem was highlighted by an attempt by national government to start a register of 'approved' contractors, which has been tested in Birmingham. It has not been very successful because there is a charge to register, and the very contractors who could have qualified had no need to be on a list to get work.

First places to look for building contractors:

- your architect
- the Yellow Pages
- local newspapers
- friends, and other self builders
- builders' merchants and product suppliers
- site boards on nearby building sites
- Internet sites that list contractors
- proactive contractors who mailshot you after your planning application is submitted
- local authority planners and building control officers (strictly unofficially)
- local authority lists of approved contractors, which are sometimes available to the public

Checking Out Building Contractors – First and Second Stages

If you are going to hand your whole project over to one building contractor, it is absolutely crucial that you engage the right company, so you must apply some tough selection criteria. With the exception of those recommended personally by someone you know and trust, none of the methods on the above list of places to get names are very reliable in themselves, but they should get you a reasonable shortlist to work with. The next stage is to carry out some basic checks, followed by more detailed scrutiny of those who look like the best prospects.

First stage: a phone call

Can you easily get a full name and address?

If there is only a mobile phone number, and further details are not immediately proffered, cross them off straight away. If they do give an address, is it their home number or do they have a yard and an office?

Membership of organisations

There are a plethora of organisations for builders to join, some which require members to fulfil conditions, others that just have a membership fee. There is a rule of thumb that says that the elaborateness of the logo is inversely proportionate to the value of the organisation, which is slightly unfair but contains a germ of truth. The truly professional organisations that builders may belong to are the RICS (Royal Institute of Chartered Surveyors) and the CIOB (Chartered Institute of Building). The other builders' organisations are effectively clubs. Although they sometimes make fairly grand claims, membership of them should not be seen as any kind of guarantee of a quality service.

Track record

How long has their company been in existence? This is different to how long they have been in business. Some organisations have a habit of winding up their business and 'phoenixing' the next day by starting a new company with a very similar name, and the same staff and offices. This way they avoid all the debts and legal liabilities incurred by their previous incarnation.

Staff

How many permanent staff do they employ, as opposed to part-timers and contract workers. If their management team is one person, what happens when that person goes on holiday or is sick?

Availability

Most good building contractors are booked up at least several months ahead. Some are booked up for 12 months by the end of the winter. So, if they are available next week, ask them why. Sometimes there is a genuine reason – typically that an expected contract has fallen through, leaving a sudden gap in their workload.

Behaviour and communication

If their representative doesn't listen properly, uses unnecessary jargon, or is evasive when asked straight questions, put a big question mark next to them, and ask to talk to someone else if they are not in charge. If they make you uneasy in the space of a telephone call, think how you would feel after a six-month building project.

Readiness to quote

Make it clear that you will require a fixed price, and will be using an industry-standard contract. If they are reluctant to agree to the former, cross them off the list immediately. They may start with a low price to get you interested and you will pay far more by the end of the project. If they object and try to persuade you that you don't need a contract, bear in mind that most decent contractors prefer a proper written contract. If a building contractor suggests that you should use their own contract, get professional advice. The ones that are written in tiny grey ink on the back of a quote are usually heavily biased against their customers.

Builder v Architect

Likewise, if they try to persuade you that you don't need an architect or other professional to inspect on your behalf, and that this way you will save money, think very carefully. It may be that your architect has somehow not given you good value for money. But some contractors like to separate their clients from a source of independent advice, giving them more freedom to charge for extras, and to avoid quality control on site.

At the end of the phone call ask them to send you some information on their company by post, but do not be too disappointed if you receive little or nothing. Many building contractors who are excellent builders are hopeless at marketing, because it is not a necessary skill; as long as they have happy clients, there will always be work waiting to be done. Conversely, slick marketing brochures and flashy websites have occasionally been found to conceal a business that cannot get work any other way. Once you have weeded out the dubious names on the list, you can move to the next stage, and look a little more closely at the ones that are left.

No contractor should make it on to your tender list unless you are quite sure that, based on what you know so far, you would use them if theirs was the most favourable tender. You may leave some of the second-stage checks until after you have got prices back, to save time, but proper checks are essential before you commit yourself by signing a contract.

Second stage: research and visiting
Where do they work?

Insist on visiting their offices. If they won't invite you, find an excuse to go – however briefly. In all likelihood it will not be a palace, but you will get a good picture of who you are dealing with. If their office is based at home, the size of the house and make of car may tell you a bit about the profit margins the company works to.

References and portfolio

When you go to see them, ask to see photos of examples of their work, find out where these are, and then ask for references. Visit the properties, and talk to the clients. A short chat over the phone will tell you more than written recommendations.

Insurance

All building contractors must have public liability insurance, and the insurance necessary to run a construction site. It is acceptable to ask the contractor to confirm that these are in place, and for what amounts. You can ask for actual documentary proof before you sign the contract.

Management

There are many ways to evade taxes and reduce costs by ignoring legislation. If you get a wink and nod that you can save some money these ways from a general contractor, do not use their services. If they will cheat the taxman, they may cheat you too. The main reason construction sites kill so many people every year is because these sort of employers fail to comply with the health and safety laws. You could become one of those statistics if you allow your builder to cut corners.

How to Spot a 'Cowboy'

- no business address
- no proper telephone number
- use of logos on their letterhead that they are not entitled to
- history of regularly winding up companies
- immediate availability with no explanation
- poor standard of behaviour by staff
- reluctance to use a standard contract
- reluctance to work with your professional team
- very few, or no, previous clients who you can speak to directly
- no insurance certificates
- attempts to dodge tax
- unrealistically low quote
- accompanied by a 'minder' wherever they go

Fortunately – in spite of the pitfalls, and contrary to the popular image of the small building contractor – there are many excellent ones to be found, who take great personal pride in their work, deal honestly with their customers, and who leave nothing but well-built family homes in their wake. If you get one of these firms, you will find the experience of working with them on a building site an educational and enjoyable experience.

Self-Managing Subcontractors

If you are not going to use a single main contractor, but wish to organise your own site, you need a different tack to deal with the trades whom you will employ. Some of the methods that have been suggested for general contractors will work, but there are important differences. These people (and they are often just people, not businesses as such) are harder to find, and owe their true loyalty to their regular employers – the contractors who use them as part of a building team. They may not agree to a written contract, and any written record will probably have to be made by you. They will expect to be paid weekly, not in stages like a main contractor, and they will probably want cash.

The best way to find them is through other self builders, but often the only way to find out if they are any good is to actually take them on and sack them if you are unhappy. It is a daunting task to get good workers, because even the established contractors complain that there are not enough reliable people around, and fewer and fewer younger people are moving into the construction industry to replace the skilled older generation.

Getting a Price for the Work

Once you have a list of contractors that has satisfied you and your architect, you are ready to send out the tender documents. Once tenders are invited, at least three or four weeks should be allowed for prices to arrive. This is because contractors tend to deal with pricing in between all their site-related jobs for the day, and also because they will, in turn, put some of the work out to tender from their regular subcontractors – and this procedure takes time.

During the tender process it is essential that all contractors receive exactly the same information, and that any extra details or changes are confirmed in writing to all of them together. This is the only way that the prices received can be accurately compared. It is also important that they are not told who the other contractors on the list are. This is because, by anticipating their competitors' pricing policies, it is possible for them to adjust their tender price accordingly. They may find out anyway, through the suppliers of products you have specified, or through subcontractors who are asked to quote for your project by more than one contractor.

Contractors must be asked to state the following in their tenders: a fixed price, how long they will take to complete the work, and when they can start.

A Typical Tender Package

A typical tender package will contain:

- a letter inviting tenders
- a form for replying to tender invitation
- a tender-return envelope
- a set of 1:50 plans and elevations
- one or two 1:20 sections
- some 1:5 details
- a detailed specification (e.g. twenty A4 pages)

Opening the Tenders

There is a certain amount of protocol to follow if you wish to do this correctly. In larger organisations there are set procedures, which are rigidly applied to reduce the chance of corruption. These stipulate that all the tenders must be opened at the exact time that has been stated in the invitation to tender. Any late tenders are disposed of without being opened, and the contractor that has submitted the most appropriate tender on paper has to be given the job. It is impractical to apply these rules to your self-build project, but it is important to be fair, and to be seen to be fair. If you grant an extension to one contractor, allow the same for all of them. You can put a simple code on the return envelope to identify who has sent it, so if someone is a bit late, you can phone them to check what has happened without opening the other tenders. If there are two contractors who are so close that it is difficult to choose between them, treat them equally, and give them the same chance to have a go at reducing their costs or revising their timescale.

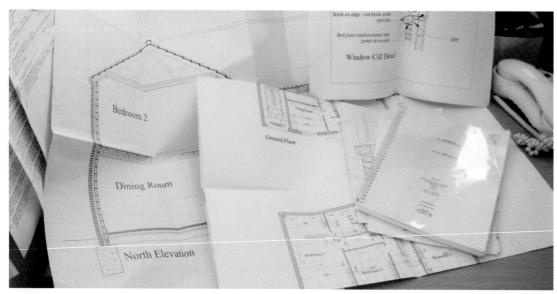

Typical Tender Package.

Checking Out Building Contractors – Third Stage

Third stage: after tenders

Hopefully, you will filter out any problem contractors before they are invited to tender, and have on your list only the best available companies. But when you receive prices back, you should consider the following:

Are their sums right?

Before the lowest tender can be confirmed, the chosen building contractor should be asked provide a detailed price breakdown. This is to reduce the possibility that they have made a mistake in their calculations, and to allow stage payments to be calculated.

Have they been thorough?

As the contractors carry out their costing exercise during the tender period, they will inevitably pick up small errors or ambiguities in the tender documents, or want clarification on particular points. If a contractor has been in touch with questions before submitting their price, this is a very good sign. If they have not, it is a sign either that they worked out their price very late in the day, that they have not worked out a price in sufficient detail, or that they have guessed the answers to the questions that arose.

 Issue a written 'tender update' to all tenderers if you have given any extra information whilst talking to one of them – and do this before the date on which tenders have to be submitted. Otherwise, some of the tenders will be based on different information to others and cannot be easily compared.

What to Do If You Go Over Budget

To start with, be reassured that you are in good company – including not only lots of other self builders, but also many large construction projects which have huge teams of experienced professional advisors working on them. Secondly, don't panic. It is possible to reduce costs significantly, unless you have been grossly over-optimistic.

Over-specification

The main reason that a project goes over budget is that the specification is too high. In other words, you have chosen too many nice things – understandable before you know exactly how much they will cost. If this is your problem, it is painful but relatively easy to solve. You will have to cut some things out and reduce the cost of others. The very last things to cut are those which make up the main fabric of the building, unless they are particularly extravagant. You cannot save up and easily replace the bricks, roof tiles or internal walls with better ones in the future.

Wrong Contractors

Sometimes, not enough prices come back, or the ones that do are from contractors who are not that keen to get the work. Re-tendering to a fresh set of contractors can help in these situations. It is a step worth taking before you give up on a project. All you have to lose is the cost of the extra tender packages and a few weeks, and you may get better prices the second time around.

Inflation

Even the Chancellor of the Exchequer doesn't really know what will happen to the economy between the start of your project, when you do your initial budget calculation, and later stages, when you find out what builders are proposing to charge you for it. But your professional advisors should be able to give you updates as the design progresses. If you are lucky, you may get a better deal from your mortgage provider to compensate for any adverse economic effects.

Building Too Large

If the building is far too big, then you will have to consider omitting parts of the house, redesigning, or abandoning the project and hoping to sell on the house design as part of the package to the new owner of the land. You should, however, have been aware of this risk well before you submitted your planning application – so, provided that you have not been assuming excessively over-optimistic budget costs, you should not have reached this point. It is actually quite rare for things to get this bad.

Where to Save Money

Decorations and Finishes

- Reduce the number of different colours.
- Take out any special finishes, stick to plain white where you can stand it.
- Do the internal decoration yourself.
- Take out laminate floors and quarry tiles, and use basic vinyl and carpet until you can afford to upgrade.

Internal Doors and Ironmongery

- Cheap internal doors can be replaced very easily in the future, one at a time as you can afford it if necessary. Keep the better-standard doors for where they are most on show, e.g. those that are off the hallway, and use cheap flush doors elsewhere.

Kitchens

- Large sums can be saved by fitting a cheaper kitchen, which can be replaced later. If you were planning to use a specialist contractor, get the main contractor to suggest an alternative specification. There are huge discounts available to many contractors on standard ranges of fittings.

Joinery, Skirtings and Trims

- If there is any fancy joinery, simplify it.
- Replace hardwood with softwood.
- Built-in cupboards and wardrobes can be taken out of the contract and replaced with free-standing furniture.

Electrical Installations

- The difference between a desirable electrical layout and a serviceable one is often significant. Reduce the number of sockets.
- Use cheaper light fittings, which can be easily replaced as long as the concealed wiring is in the right position.

Sanitaryware

- This is often an item where fantasy can overtake rational thought, and the reduction of the specification to cheaper models is relatively easy to achieve.

Special Features

- If you selected underfloor heating, central vacuum cleaning, solar panels, or expensive fire surrounds, this is the point at which to reassess how badly you want them.

Garage and Conservatory

- If parts of the building can easily be removed without distorting or spoiling the plan, savings can be made. Provided you have made a substantial start on a building with full permission, you will have planning approval to build them any time you choose in the future.

External Works

- Replacing the concrete-block paving in the drive with gravel can save thousands of pounds.
- Omitting the pond, or delaying planting out until the following year will also contribute a big saving.

Construction

After many months – or even years – of preparation, you will reach the final and most crucial stage of the project: the building work itself. The success or failure of the construction stage will probably have been decided well before you reach this point. Things will go wrong, because that's what happens on a building site – even the best planning in the world cannot cover every eventuality. But if you accept that there will be problems, and have an idea of how they will be dealt with, you have every chance of dealing with them successfully. All of this section applies if you are using a single main contractor, but much of it also applies if you are self managing or doing much of the work yourself.

Summary of This Stage:

- Agreeing the Building Contract
- Preparing for Work to Start
- Building Your Home
- Reaching Completion

Agreeing the Building Contract

Never, ever, agree to engage a main contractor without a proper written contract from an independent source. It is not necessary to employ a solicitor to draft one especially for you – there are plenty of standard contracts, some of which have been developed by committees with representatives from all the main bodies involved in the construction industry. (The best-known of these is the Joint Contracts Tribunal, or JCT.) They are fair to all sides, and are specifically designed to anticipate the most likely problems and stipulate how they should be dealt with.

A contract often used by architects is 'JCT Minor Works', but there are others that are similar. On signing the contract, the employer (you) takes on certain duties, mainly concerned with payment, and also takes the ultimate responsibility and risk for the contract. Much of the work can be delegated to the architect, if you employ one to help on site. In this respect, building your home is very different from buying a house from a developer and being simply 'a customer'. After you have signed a contract, and everyone is clear about their responsibilities, it can be put away and hopefully not have to be referred to again.

Make sure that you explain to tendering contractors which contract you will want them to use – and the main points of it, such as liquidated damages, etc. Otherwise, the lowest contractor may use the introduction of a contract as the basis to renegotiate the price.

The Key Terms of a Building Contract

The Parties

This is you, and the builder. You may think it is obvious, but some builders have more than one company. And sometimes parties to contracts have used the fact that have been wrongly described to avoid their liabilities.

The Identification of the Works

Particularly important if the contractor takes on other work outside this contract, e.g. the landscaping.

The Contract Documents

It is essential to state the specific drawings, by number and revision letter, as well as the version of the specification. These may be different from the tender documents if a price-cutting exercise has been carried out.

The Professionals

If you are using an architect or similar professional to manage the contract on your behalf, you must make clear what powers they have in the contract. You should also have a matching, separate agreement with this contract manager.

The Tender Sum

This has to tie in directly with the contract documents, and must reflect any post-tender changes.

The Project Duration and Liquidated Damages

Many of the problems that arise between client and builder are due to overruns. The contract should clearly state the time that work is to start, and when it is to be finished. A useful clause to have is one that states that any unwarranted delays will give you the right to make deductions from money due to the builder, usually a set amount for each week. These payments are known as 'liquidated damages'.

Payment Terms

Contractors are usually paid every four weeks, or at specific stages in the job, e.g. upon reaching damp-proof course level. Also, a small amount is held back until the end of the job – usually 5 per cent of the tender sum. A smaller amount is kept until six months after work is finished (usually 2.5 per cent).

Insurance

The contractor must have, and maintain, adequate insurance. But this will probably not be extended to cover items that belong exclusively to you and are stored on site, unless you ask for this.

Solving Disputes

There should be a description of what parties can do if there is a dispute, and what to do if it cannot be settled.

Preparing for Work to Start

Once the contract is signed, you are almost ready for building work to start. But there are a few matters to be dealt with first.

Where will you live?

You will probably have made this decision much earlier, but may have modified your plans in the light of the tenders that you received. The ideal is to remain in your existing house for the duration of the project, but many people cannot afford to do this. The next-best option is to rent a house somewhere near the site, or move into your parents' home. For those who have a very limited budget, and are able to take the stress, mobile homes can be rented and fixed up with plumbing and mains services. The latter should only be taken on if all members of the family agree, and have realistic expectations of the quality of life that they will experience.

Whatever the build programme says, regardless of whether you or a firm of experienced contractors have prepared it, always allow for at least a 20 per cent overrun, and have contingency plans for if it is longer. If you are building or managing yourself, allow for a 50 per cent overrun.

Start a Site File

During construction, efficient management of information will be helpful. If you have not already done so, create a project file with the following sections for correspondence and notes:

- in the front, a sheet of contact details of everyone involved
- copy of contract documents
- site meetings
- client
- architect
- engineer
- contractor
- planning
- building regulations
- utilities
- suppliers and manufacturers

Pre-Contract Meeting

Before a contractor occupies the site, it is a good idea to have a meeting to discuss the way that the project is to be run, which is sometimes combined with the contract-signing. It is important that you are reassured that this project, which is to be run in your name, will be well managed and will cause as little inconvenience to your neighbours as possible. Most importantly of all, the site must be as safe as possible.

The best-run projects are based on good communication between all parties, and this is an opportune time to arrange some regular project team meetings, with someone making notes or taking minutes. You do not necessarily have to be present at all of them if you are using an architect to manage on your behalf, but you need to be kept informed of all the important discussions.

Standard Agenda for Pre-Contract Meeting

1. Introductions. Full names and contact details of everyone present.

2. Contract

1. Commencement and Completion dates
2. Programme. Detailed breakdown of each trade and subcontractor.
3. Insurance. Ask for photocopies of the relevant documents.
4. Building Regulations. Check that the building control officer will be notified.

3. Site

1. Sign boards. Where will they be erected?
2. Storage. This can take up a significant portion of the site.

4. Communications

1. Contractor contact on site. Name and mobile-phone number.
2. Client contact. Which member of your family is to be the main contact?

5. Information

1. Information required. The contractor may need further drawings or specifications to progress the work.
2. Details of subcontractors – names and addresses.

6. Certificates

Every four weeks, or stage-payments?

7. Health and Safety

What measures will the contractor have in place to manage health and safety? Is there a risk that the site may be easily accessible to children and other members of the general public, and will steps be taken to keep it secure?

Make sure that all the original contract documents are signed by both parties, with initials on each drawing, and that they are kept separately, away from the project files. If there are any disagreements about extras, etc. you will need to refer back to them.

Building Your Home

Starting to Build

Don't be surprised if at 8.00 a.m. on the day work is due to start, no-one turns up. The contractor is committed to a completion date and has a right to start on the contractually agreed date, but not an obligation. A diligent builder will make sure that the last job is properly finished before moving on to the next – an attitude that you may be grateful for when it is your turn. A telephone call at 8.30 a.m. demanding to know where the workforce have got to will not help diplomatic relations.

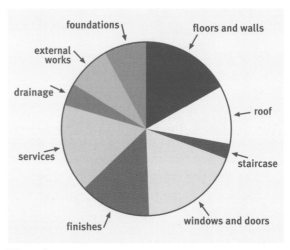

Where the money goes.

Planning approvals often have conditions, such as that brick types or a landscaping design be submitted and approved 'before work commences'. Don't forget to get these discharged before the building control officer is notified of work starting.

Table 14: A Typical Build Programme								
Weeks	1	4	8	12	16	20	24	28
Groundworks	■							
Brickwork		■	■					
Roof			■					
Carpentry			■		■			
Electrics				■				
Plumbing				■		■		
Plasterwork/Screed				■				
Decorations				■		■		
External works						■		

As well as the photos and video recordings that you will inevitably want to take of progress, keep a job diary, recording you visits and what stage the work has reached. If you are not satisfied with progress later on, or if there are arguments about what was discussed or agreed, notes made at the time, however rough, will carry a lot of weight.

Take regular photographs of the work as it progresses, and record the dates.

Once construction starts, a main contractor takes legal possession of the site. This means that it is effectively sub-let to the contractor and even you, the owner, should technically ask for permission to visit.

Five Golden Rules for a Building Project:

1. Never pay in advance, except for specialist items.
2. Agree dates for payment before work starts.
3. Make regular visits to site for quality control.
4. Always record key events in writing.
5. Make the builder quote a completion date, and try to hold him to it.

Certificates

Most people know that a newly built house needs a certificate, but there is often uncertainty about what one actually is. Building societies require some kind of certification before they will release payments. If you sell the house within ten years or so of finishing it, the purchaser's solicitor will ask for a copy of the certificate. A lot of confusion is caused by building societies making no distinction between architects' certificates and building warranties – but in fact they are quite different.

Architects' Interim Certificates

These are issued by the architect at regular intervals throughout the building programme – either every four weeks, or when key stages are reached. Interim Certificates have only one purpose. Once issued, you have to pay the contractor for the work that he has completed to date, provided that it is satisfactory. Because they are interim, they are not proof that the work has been completed properly, and you retain the right to withhold money later on if there are any hidden defects. However, because the architect can hold back payment if there is anything that is not up to standard, the architect has the power to ensure that the work meets the required standard, and to refuse to pay for it until it is right. As a further safeguard, the architect deducts 5 per cent from the value of the work completed, which you retain until later on.

Interim Certificates help you to plan your cash flow, but most of all they ensure that the contractor knows that their progress and workmanship are being closely monitored.

Suggested Key Stages for Interim Payments:

1. Damp-proof course height, including the drainage backfilled, passed by the building control officer and structural ground-floor slab in position.
2. First-floor wall-plate height achieved, first-floor structure in place.
3. Building watertight.
4. Immediately prior to second-fix of electrics and plumbing.
5. Completion.

Inspection/Valuation Certificates

Some building societies have their own certificates, which they may ask you to use. So, if they are going to be signed by the architect, make sure that the wording is acceptable to them – ideally before you engage one to work for you. These certificates protect the building society's or lender's investment, rather than your interests. They are chiefly concerned that the construction value of the building is monitored – not, for example, whether the right colour bathroom has been fitted.

Practical Completion Certificates

For most self builders, the date that they can occupy the house is crucial. This is usually referred to as Practical Completion, and should be recorded in the contract that you both sign. Some contracts state that it is for the architect to decide whether or not this completion date has been achieved. If it has been achieved, the Practical Completion Certificate can be issued. If there is a liquidated damages clause, and the contractor has not provided a good explanation as to why there is an overrun, you have the option of deducting money in compensation, although this is not recommended except as a last resort.

There is a lot of argument as to how to accurately define 'Practical Completion', but it can be described as the time when you can live in the building without serious inconvenience from building work. This may mean that the builder has to finish minor outstanding items, all of which may be listed along with the certificate. So you can move in without waiting for every last detail to be finished.

You can build in a safeguard against any outstanding items not being finished, or hidden defects not immediately apparent appearing at a later date. Release half of the 5 per cent you have been holding back, leaving 2.5 per cent to be retained for six months. After this time, any defects that become apparent have to be made good before the final amount is paid over.

Final Certificate

The Final Certificate is normally issued after six months of occupation. Before the architect signs it, the contractor must make good any defects or errors which may have become apparent after you moved in. He is then entitled to the final 2.5 per cent of the contract value, which you have kept until this point.

Final Certificates are often at the core of a misunderstanding between architects and their clients. Some clients believe that they are getting a guarantee that the building is free from all defects. In fact, the only person in a position to be sure of this is someone who has continuously supervised the purchase of materials, and the workmen on site, every day for the entire project – in short, a main contractor. An architect's certificate is not in any sense a guarantee.

What an architect actually does is 'inspect generally the progress and quality of the work'. This means that extensive training and specialist knowledge are deployed throughout the building programme to protect your interests. As a legal minimum, a professional person is expected to use the skill and care of the average competent practitioner, although if you choose your architect carefully, you will hopefully get better than the average.

Building society inspections are unlikely, in themselves, to be sufficient to prevent many of the day-to-day problems that might arise on site, which would be pre-empted by the regular site visits carried out as part of a full service from an architect.

Other Forms of Certification

If you do not wish to use an independent professional, or one is not available, the alternative is to use a building warranty. These are offered by organisations such as the National House-Building Council (NHBC) and Zurich Municipal, and are backed by insurance underwriters. There are many varieties available, which cover all situations – from a house being built by a DIY self builder, to one completed by a professional team. So if you are using the latter, make sure that the builder is registered to qualify for cover.

The inspections undertaken by these organisations are fairly limited, and will not necessarily prevent problems. They will cover you for catastrophic failures, such as the builder going bust or bits of the house falling off, but very often they will not pay for rectification of defects that they consider 'minor', particularly if the problems only come to light several years after completion.

The Ideal Combination

Building warranties are a safety net against the worst happening; and architects' certificates prove that a professional, who should have reduced the risk of problems developing in the first place, has been involved on site. The most prudent course is to obtain both, although there will be a higher cost. Some of the warranty providers do expect that you should at least have a professional advisor to hand once work starts on site, and even that the drawings and specification can be shown to have been prepared by someone who is appropriately qualified.

No certificate – whether issued by an architect, on behalf of lenders, or by the NHBC – will guarantee that your building will be perfect. Architects' certificates, issued as part of a total package of managing a building contract, are designed to increase your control at the same time as reducing the risk of problems developing after the building is completed.

The Architect's Role on Site

If a full service has been chosen, the architect will inspect once every two weeks or so on average, instruct alterations and issue extra information if necessary. If work is unsatisfactory in the opinion of the architect, the contractor has to rebuild or correct it. All queries, variations to the work and instructions to the contractor should theoretically go through the architect – although, in practice, clients tend to issue instructions directly, and this is workable provided that the architect is kept informed before the work is carried out.

Building Your Home/Reaching Completion

An architect, or similar professional, inspecting on site should pick up defects such as these early, and get them put right.

However, confusion can result if the client issues instructions directly to the contractor or tradesmen on site, without informing the architect. There may be an extra cost involved as a result of the instruction, or perhaps implications for the rest of the design. If the instruction is not recorded properly, confusion may result later on. The architect might even be able to suggest an alternative solution to a problem being raised.

What if Something Goes Wrong on Site?

A one-off house is a prototype, and the one thing that is certain is that some things will not go according to plan. Part of the management of the project should be assuming that this will be the case. With careful planning, the right advice, and a bit of luck, nothing serious will happen. If it does, and you are at risk of being out of pocket, you will need to take action. Unless there is no alternative, it is by far the best solution to remain on speaking terms with everyone involved, and to get the problem sorted out before you start to attach blame. If you have used one of the standard contracts, there will be provisions that set out what you can do if you reach an impasse – like start an adjudication, which is a quick, often temporary, fix. The alternative might be to embark on legal action, which is far more lengthy and expensive, and should be a last resort, ideally not to be embarked on before the work has been completed.

The Contractor

If you are unhappy with the contractor, bear in mind that, unless you are approaching the end of the project, it will be a major disaster for you if they walk out on the job, however much they are in the wrong. Get professional help and advice, if you are not already using it. Ask the senior management to change the site operatives if you have a problem with an individual. If you or your architect decide to hold back payment, make sure that you follow the rules set out in the contract to the letter. If you want to throw the contractor off the site, do not do so without consulting a solicitor. However distressing it gets, as long as you are not paying anyone in advance, you have the upper hand financially. Remember that the contractor has a lot to lose as well, and will be just as keen as you to set things right.

Your Professional Advisors

If you employ an architect, they must have professional indemnity insurance, and they must have a detailed, written appointment letter. But if they make a mistake that costs you money, you may have to prove that negligence has occurred before their insurance company will pay out.

Reaching Completion

The building work may have been continuously monitored by the builder's management team, yourself, the building control officer and possibly your architect as well, but once the contractor tells you that the work is

finished, arrange a formal inspection tour. You should have a defects period agreed, and hold a retention on any amount due, but once the builder leaves the site it is harder to get any faults put right quickly. In theory, you should not have to 'snag' a building, because it is supposed to be complete, but, even if the work has been immaculate, your idea of a 'defect' may not be seen as faults by others. An architect administering the contract has the power to have anything put right that, in their opinion, is unsatisfactory. Unsurprisingly, the process of snagging can lead to disagreements, and it is not in your interests to fall out with the contractor at this stage. If the work has been of a good standard so far, a little tact will go a long way, but do not be afraid to insist if there is something that you are unhappy with. You will probably be looking at it every day for the next few years, and however trivial it may appear to anyone else, you will always see it. It is not necessarily a defence for the contractor that it has been there for several weeks, or even months – any interim payments are not legally conclusive evidence that you or your architect have approved the work.

Less-reputable foremen prefer to let a lot of snags go, get the architect or client to do all the snagging and see what they can get away with. If there are a lot of snags, it is advisable to halt the meeting, refuse to accept completion, ask the contractor to tell you when the building is really finished, then leave.

Snagging Checklist

Pitched Roof

- roof slates or tiles undamaged, unmarked and properly bedded?

- vent tiles/eaves in place, fly-screens fitted?

- main edges, such as the ridge and line of the eaves, straight?

- flashings in place and properly fixed, with adequate lap and wedged into brickwork?

- weep holes above cavity trays, dpc and openings

- ventilation openings adequate?

Rainwater Drainage

- valley gutters clean and free from debris?

- gutters and stop-ends located correctly, sufficient brackets, and falls in right directions?

- gutters clear of rubbish?

- roof underlay laps into gutter?

Brickwork

- pointing complete, gaps created by scaffolding made good?

- clean, no mortar splashes?

- mortar and brickwork consistent in colour?

- perpends line through neatly?

Downpipes

- fixed properly?

- locations match the drawings?

Overflow pipes

- visible?

- correct length?

- sealed around, and watertight, at exit point?

Windows and Doors Externally

- no chips or splits, or other damage

- window frames sealed at edges?

- glass cleaned, and not scratched?

- beading securely fixed?

- front door wide enough for a wheelchair?

Paintwork and Staining

- finished with all coats, especially where hidden, e.g. tops of doors, under window sills?

External Landscaping

- level access to the front door or, if not possible, at another entry to main living level?

- no bumps or unplanned steps

- ground level minimum 150 mm below dpc height?

- all slopes fall away from the building?

- manhole covers and inspection hatches in good condition and fitting properly?

- boundary walls straight, properly built, with openings and dpcs?

Construction

Reaching Completion

Ceilings

- corners are straight?

Paintwork

- all coats of paints applied?
- free from patches?
- cleaned down?
- smooth surface, free of plasterboard joints and cracks?

Plasterwork

- smooth, even surfaces?
- gaps made good around services penetrations?
- junctions and corners straight?

Windows Internally

- painted properly?
- timberwork undamaged?
- no scratches or marks on the glass?
- open and close smoothly?
- no distortion in the frame?
- trickle ventilators working?
- compliance with escape requirements on first floor and above?
- locks on ground-floor windows

Doors Internally

- painted properly?
- timberwork undamaged?
- open and shut when handle turned?
- don't pull open without operating the handle?
- no distortion in the frame?
- door has an equal gap around the frame?
- garage door fire-rated with self closer and step?
- ironmongery and locks clean and as specified, and working properly?

Skirtings and Architraves

- undamaged, no dents, marks and painted properly?

Floor Finishes

- tiling complete, even, regularly spaced, and sealed at joints?
- vinyl smooth and even, with no bubbles or lumps?
- clean?
- concrete floor smooth, clean and ready for carpet, etc?

Services

- pipes supported with plenty of clips?
- radiators securely fixed, clean, with bleed points accessible?
- switches and sockets clean, level and secure?

Staircases

- balustrading, newels, handrails securely fixed?
- surface varnish or paint complete, clean and undamaged?
- equal risers and goings?

Kitchens and Bathrooms

- all fittings clean, working, and without chips or blemishes?
- taps working?
- toilets flush?
- plugs and other attachments present?
- no leaks to plumbing?
- worktops unblemished?
- cupboard doors fitted square and secure?

Plumbing

- no leaks?
- securely fixed?

Electrical

- all fitted appliances working (e.g. cooker, heaters)?
- mechanical ventilation working?

Gas and Fires

- appliances operating properly?
- ventilation available, as required by Building Regulations?

Before you let the contractor leave the site, ask for all the documents that will help you, and future owners, maintain the building – covering aspects such as:

- heating, including SAP calculation
  (Standard Assessment Procedure – the rating of a building's insulation levels)
- alarm system
- appliances
- electrical layout and fittings
- 'As-built' drawings.

Also make sure that you have the names and addresses of all the key suppliers and subcontractors, some of whom may agree to come back for routine maintenance.

You also need to be sure that all the necessary approvals and certificates are in place, along with any suppliers'/manufacturers' guarantees, such as those for:

- Building Control Certificate of Completion
- central heating
- IEE Electrical Certificate
- appliances
- laminate and other specialist floors
- any specialist features or components

After Completion

Once the building is agreed to be 'practically complete' you can occupy it, and start to turn it into a home. But, as you start to live in it, there will probably be some defects, or small faults that need to be rectified. A 2.5 per cent retention should be kept for six months after completion, for what is called the 'Latent Defects Period'. During this time, any defects that arise as result of the construction must be put right by the contractor.

During the contract, there will have been changes and modifications to the design, unexpected extras, and other matters that will have caused the original contract value to be amended. It is not unusual for the contractor to still be calculating and agreeing these with you well into the defects liability period. Hopefully, by the time this period has ended you will have agreed the amount due, and a 'Final Account' can be prepared to tie up all the loose ends. If the contractor has done a good job, worked hard, and delivered the project to you more or less on time, the decent thing is not to haggle too much over minor items. At the end of the project, you should look at the whole picture. If you have got a good building, at a decent price, the builder probably deserves what they are asking for. Trying to reduce the bill as much as possible is mean, especially if they have not taken every opportunity to claim extras.

 Make sure that you have all the information you will need from the contractor for regular maintenance and future alterations and improvements to the house before you pay the final bill, and keep it together safely in a single file.

At the end of the six months, the architect will carry out a final inspection, and note any defective work that needs to be put right. After this has been done, you pay the final amounts to both architect and contractor, and, with any luck, that should be the end of your building project.

Case Studies

There are thousands of successful individual homes built every year. Each one has a story behind it, and every tale is different. It is surprising how people with broadly similar backgrounds, family circumstances and incomes can produce such a wide variety of designs and styles. These examples are taken from all over the country, and all of them demonstrate how good buildings result from a successful collaboration between architect and client. These houses reflect the people who instigated them, their locations, and various problems that were tackled and solved.

Summary of This Stage:

- House for Mr and Mrs Jackson, Richmond, North Yorkshire
- House for Mr and Mrs Nicholson, Kirkliston, Lothian, Scotland
- House for Mr and Mrs Bowles, Ely, Cambridgeshire
- House for Mr and Mrs Baker, Devon
- House for Mr and Mrs Cook, East Sussex

House for Mr and Mrs Jackson, Richmond, North Yorkshire

Architect: John Sheldrake RIBA of Cleveland Architectural Design

Architect's Service: Design, Planning application, Building Regulations application and site certificates

Build Method: Self managed

Construction: Bespoke timber frame

Time from site acquisition to building completion: 12 months

Build Programme: 5–6 months

Mr and Mrs Jackson spent a lot of time doing their research, by visiting numerous self-build shows and looking in magazines. They got the names of several architects, including, via the ASBA freephone service, Cleveland Architectural Design. They interviewed three designers, but hit it off with John Sheldrake almost immediately – 'his attitude and aspirations matched ours', says Tim Jackson. They had acquired an L-shaped plot that was originally part of a barracks, which is now a housing estate. The plot had been rejected by developers because of its awkward shape, and the neighbours were delighted when they heard that a house was going to be built on what had become abandoned waste ground. Because the site was elevated

House for Mr and Mrs Jackson.

above its surroundings, the windows had to be carefully designed to allow in maximum light without overlooking the neighbouring properties or compromising their privacy.

Richmond, North Yorkshire/Kirkliston, Lothian

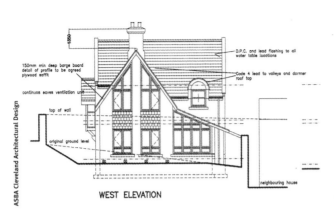

WEST ELEVATION

ASBA Cleveland Architectural Design

Elevation showing the feature windows.

The Jacksons' brief was quite specific about their requirements for the house, including the need both for a dedicated music room and to take advantage of the spectacular view on one side, but they left it to the architect to come up with the design. They approved the first scheme presented, which they think elegantly fitted 'a quart into a pint pot'. A timber frame was selected, and a high level of insulation was achieved using a product made from recycled paper.

Photo: Carolyn Tame

The main bedroom has a spectacular view.

The local authority planning department had no problems with the design, although the drawings were scrutinised closely (possibly because one of the planners drove past the site regularly on the way to his golf club). The planners' concerns regarding the detailed construction were addressed by incorporating some of the traditional building features from houses in the nearby town, which were expertly blended with the more modern features such as the triangular windows. Mr and Mrs Jackson are very happy with the finished building. It was built on budget and the house is now worth considerably more than it cost to build.

House for Mr and Mrs Nicholson, Kirkliston, Lothian, Scotland

Architect: Walter Wood Associates, Edinburgh

Architect's Service: Sketch design, planning application, Building Regulations application, tender, contract management and certification

Build Method: Single main contractor

Construction: Bespoke timber frame, sitting on a masonry basement

Time taken to find site: 3 years

Time from site acquisition to building completion: 18 months

Build Programme: 10 months

Mr and Mrs Nicholson found their site by accident. Whilst investigating another plot, which turned out to be unsuitable, the estate agents told them about another one on their books – an existing house with outline planning approval for a one-and-a-half storey chalet bungalow in its garden. In

Scotland, a bid for a property has to be submitted by a set date and is usually binding if the vendor then accepts it. In this instance, because the Nicholsons had stipulated that they must to be able to build a two-storey house, the vendor allowed them time to talk to the planning department and establish that this would be permissible. It was, and the house and plot were acquired. As they gathered more detailed information on prices, they realised that their original budget was over-optimistic, so they increased it to a level that was realistic for the Edinburgh area.

Mr Nicholson had wanted to build a house for 20 years, and throughout this time he built up considerable knowledge of the options available. He first came across the architect, ASBA director Walter Wood, as an agent for a timber-kit company. Although the kit company now no longer trades in the UK, he kept Walter's details. Client and architects worked well together, the design concept being triggered by an illustration kept by Mr Nicholson from a book on American-style houses, which was developed into what he calls an 'elegant solution'.

The house has a striking exterior.

A central part of the design thinking was to incorporate ecologically sound and sustainable building techniques as much as possible. This helped to engender the active support of the planners for the modern design, particularly the large, wedge-shaped window, which maximises solar gain and reduces heating bills in winter. It incorporates triple glazing, and the house boasts an extra-high level of insulation in its timber-framed walls. The house was intended to be built by a single contractor, but many items were eventually stripped out of the contract as Mr Nicholson found that his own negotiating skills enabled him to reduce prices by as much as 50 per cent for items such as the kitchen and bathroom fittings and the floor tiles. The building programme was not without its stresses and strains, particularly when the roof-truss delivery was delayed by several weeks, but the family have no regrets.

The full-height glazing sits over a semi-basement level garage.

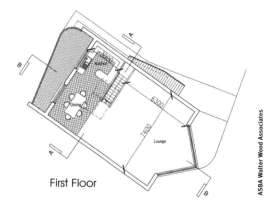

First Floor

You can tell that this is an unusual building, just from its plan.

If they ever build another house, the Nicholsons will probably self manage, using a builder for the groundworks, a timber-frame supplier for the structure, and a series of trades and specialist suppliers to finish the job.

House for Mr and Mrs Bowles, Ely, Cambridgeshire

Architect: Meredith Bowles, Mole Architects

Architect's Service: Design, Planning application, Building Regulations application, tender drawings, site certificates and contract management/contract co-ordination

Build Method: Main contractor for shell, plus other trades separately

Construction: Internal load-bearing walls plus external timber frame

Time to find site: 2 days

Time from site acquisition to building completion: 20 months

Build Programme: 10 months

The Bowles' house is uncompromisingly modern.

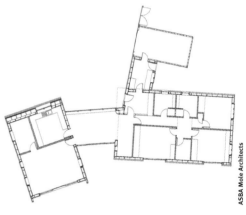

Floorplan

Within two days of Frank and Margaret Bowles making a definite start to look for a site to build their own home, they had their offer for a plot in the heart of Ely accepted. The original plan was to call in on every agent in the town, but the second one that they visited had the details of the plot pinned to the wall. Although it had been on the market for a while, there had only been two offers – both for the asking price, and both from people who had houses to sell before they could pay the money over. Having long experience of buying and selling houses, Mr Bowles immediately made a cash offer, which was accepted. Although they, too, had not yet sold their house, they had agreed a loan to buy a plot in principle with a building society beforehand, and the money was available if needed. In the event, the loan was not necessary, as they quickly sold their home and moved into more modest quarters until the project was completed.

The reason that the plot was in the agent's window for so long was that the local authority would not agree to anything but a single bungalow on this large site. This made it a poor bet for anyone trying to make a profit by developing the site and selling it on, since the combined cost of acquiring the land and then building would be in excess of the sale price. However, the Bowles do not intend to move, and were more concerned about living close to their family than making money. They had no problem finding an architect, since their son, Meredith, is the principal of ASBA member Mole Architects, based in nearby Prickwillow. Once his parents had put together some basic information on how many rooms they wanted and the approximate size of the property, Mole Architects prepared three different designs. One of them, a very modern-looking structure, clad in vertical timber boarding, with large areas of glazing facing into the garden, turned out to be ideal.

They wanted to minimise heat loss from the building and, on Meredith's suggestion, they opted for solid masonry internal walls to provide thermal mass and act as a heat sink, with highly insulated lightweight timber panels for the cladding. Although 40 x 40 m in size, the site is within a few minutes' walk of the town centre, and Ely Cathedral can easily be seen from it. Because the building is well-concealed, and single-storey, the planners did not have any real problems with the design, although they did object to the architect's proposal to clad the walls and roof of the garage with a mirror-finish metal. Early on in the design, Mr and Mrs Bowles consulted a quantity surveyor. He had just built his own house, to a traditional style and on a tight budget, and suggested some figures that later turned out to be over-optimistic. Fortunately, at the same time, the architect had also suggested some higher figures, which turned out to be nearer the mark.

In spite of the risks of conflict that could have developed by mixing family and business, all parties are very satisfied with the way that the creative process worked between architect and client, leaving them with a very special place to live.

House for Mr and Mrs Baker, Devon

Architect: David Randell Architects

Architect's Service: Design, Planning application, Building Regulations application, tender drawings, advice/call-out service on site.

Build Method: Main contractor

Construction: Green oak, fabricated and assembled on site

Build Programme: 7 months

Mr Baker, a chicken farmer, and his wife have built a house that celebrates local materials and craftsmanship. It is located between Tiverton and Bampton, in the middle of some of Devon's most picturesque countryside. The site had been part of their 70-acre smallholding for many years. The chickens need regular attention and Mr Baker decided that it was essential that he lived nearby, and he applied for permission to construct an agriculturally tied dwelling – one of the few reasons for allowing a new building in the green belt. Unfortunately, the local authority planning department were not happy with this idea, and opposed it from very early on. A battle of wills

ensued, that ended with a public enquiry into the proposal, which the Bakers won. Various conditions were made, such as a restriction to one and a half storeys in height, and a requirement for all the rainwater to be diverted into a pond on site. The latter was to be used in the event of a fire, because the house is too far away from a water supply with sufficient pressure to work a fire-fighter's hose.

Architect and builder have worked together with their client to create a genuinely traditional building.

A key priority was to create a building that not only looks traditional, but has also been constructed using traditional building techniques. The architect and craftsmen were local, and the oak that makes up the main structure was all grown and harvested within ten miles of the site. ASBA member David Randell had already designed traditional oak houses, as well as more modern timber-framed constructions, and was a natural choice as architect. David was given a free hand with the design, and came up with a scheme that makes the house look as if it has always been there. A father-and-son team of carpenters was engaged, initially just to put up the frame for a fixed price – but they did such a good job that they were asked to stay, on a dayworks basis (i.e. they were paid for their time). Traditional oak details were incorporated, right down to the windows, internal doors and wall panelling.

House for Mr and Mrs Cook, East Sussex

Architect: Julian Owen Associates, East Midlands

Architect's Service: Design, Planning application, Building Regulations application, tender drawings, contract management, certificates

Build Method: Main contractor

Construction: Brick and blockwork

Time to find plot: 4 years

Time from acquiring site to building completion: 20 months

Build Programme: 8 months

Mr and Mrs Cook approached their project with a wealth of experience, gained from renovating the various homes that they had lived in. They had long wanted to build from scratch, but had never quite found the right place to do this, despite a determined search. So they were bitterly disappointed, when, having finally located their ideal plot, they discovered that an offer from someone else had just been accepted for it. They left their details with the agent, who later got in touch when that sale fell though.

They contacted two ASBA architects, one of them based near to the site. They had seen a project in a magazine by the other one, Julian Owen Associates, that they particularly liked and, although the practice was based some distance away, met Julian Owen on site to discuss the project. They got on well and commissioned the practice. The Cooks had already assembled a formidable stack of photos, illustrations and notes, which got the briefing process off to a good start, but the biggest influence on the design was the site. It has a steep slope, and affords spectacular views across the nearby Ashdown Forest. The builders of an adjacent house had gone to a great deal of trouble and expense to cut into the slope to form a level base from which to build. Julian suggested an alterative strategy

– to use the slope as an asset and build several stepped floor levels, with a semi-basement and a projecting balcony to maximise the view. Apart from the split level inside, there is also a gallery that joins the two bedrooms in the roof space, giving views either side to the lounge and hall below.

The planning approval process was fairly straightforward, but as construction began on site the planning department tried to stop the work, complaining that the roof ridge was too high. However, the approved plans indicated no levels or datum points, and so they withdrew their argument, accepting that in the circumstances they could not impose a height limit. The original scheme was costed out by a quantity surveyor at planning stage, but once tenders were received it was clear that the estimate was too optimistic. A cost-reduction exercise was carried out in conjunction with the lowest-tendering contractor to bring down the price by 20 per cent. Some of the more ambitious design ideas were lost, such as a frameless double-height glazing panel, and the standard of finishes was also reduced, but the spirit of the building was kept intact. When the finished house was valued, it was approximately 25 per cent more than the total development cost.

The final building is a mix of contemporary style and traditional materials. The level changes, combined with large open-plan spaces and lots of natural light, give a modern feel to the interior.

The benefits of building on a sloping site here have been combined with the requirements of the clients to create an individual design.

The middle level.

Appendix

Feet/Metres Conversion (Figures in millimetres and metres)

Inches		1	2	3	4	5	6	7	8	9	10	11
Feet		25	51	76	102	127	152	178	203	229	254	279
1	305	330	356	381	406	432	457	483	508	533	559	584
2	610	635	660	686	711	737	762	787	813	838	864	889
3	914	940	965	991	1.016	1.041	1.067	1.092	1.118	1.143	1.168	1.194
4	1.219	1.245	1.270	1.295	1.321	1.346	1.372	1.397	1.422	1.448	1.473	1.499
5	1.524	1.549	1.575	1.600	1.626	1.651	1.676	1.702	1.727	1.753	1.778	1.803
6	1.829	1.854	1.880	1.905	1.930	1.956	1.981	2.007	2.032	2.057	2.083	2.108
7	2.134	2.159	2.184	2.210	2.235	2.261	2.286	2.311	2.337	2.362	2.388	2.413
8	2.438	2.464	2.489	2.515	2.540	2.565	2.591	2.616	2.642	2.667	2.692	2.718
9	2.743	2.769	2.794	2.819	2.845	2.870	2.896	2.921	2.946	2.972	2.997	3.023
10	3.048	3.073	3.099	3.124	3.150	3.175	3.200	3.226	3.251	3.277	3.302	3.327
11	3.353	3.378	3.404	3.429	3.454	3.480	3.505	3.531	3.556	3.581	3.607	3.632
12	3.658	3.683	3.708	3.734	3.759	3.785	3.810	3.835	3.861	3.886	3.912	3.937
13	3.962	3.988	4.013	4.039	4.064	4.089	4.115	4.140	4.166	4.191	4.216	4.242
14	4.267	4.293	4.318	4.343	4.369	4.394	4.420	4.445	4.470	4.496	4.521	4.547
15	4.572	4.597	4.623	4.648	4.674	4.699	4.724	4.750	4.775	4.801	4.826	4.851
16	4.877	4.902	4.928	4.953	4.978	5.004	5.029	5.055	5.080	5.105	5.131	5.156
17	5.182	5.207	5.232	5.258	5.283	5.309	5.334	5.359	5.385	5.410	5.436	5.461
18	5.486	5.512	5.537	5.563	5.588	5.613	5.639	5.664	5.690	5.715	5.740	5.766
19	5.791	5.817	5.842	5.867	5.893	5.918	5.944	5.969	5.994	6.020	6.045	6.071
20	6.096	6.121	6.147	6.172	6.198	6.223	6.243	6.274	6.299	6.325	6.350	6.375
21	6.401	6.426	6.452	6.477	6.502	6.528	6.553	6.579	6.604	6.629	6.655	6.680
22	6.706	6.731	6.756	6.782	6.807	6.833	6.858	6.883	6.909	6.934	6.960	6.985
23	7.010	7.036	7.061	7.087	7.112	7.137	7.163	7.188	7.214	7.239	7.264	7.290
24	7.315	7.341	7.366	7.391	7.417	7.442	7.468	7.493	7.518	7.544	7.569	7.595
25	7.620	7.645	7.671	7.696	7.722	7.747	7.772	7.798	7.823	7.849	7.874	7.899
26	7.925	7.950	7.976	8.001	8.026	8.052	8.077	8.103	8.128	8.153	8.179	8.204
27	8.230	8.255	8.280	8.306	8.331	8.357	8.382	8.407	8.433	8.458	8.484	8.509
28	8.534	8.560	8.585	8.611	8.636	8.661	8.687	8.712	8.738	8.763	8.788	8.814
29	8.839	8.865	8.890	8.915	8.941	8.966	8.992	9.017	9.042	9.068	9.093	9.119
30	9.144	9.169	9.195	9.220	9.246	9.271	9.296	9.322	9.347	9.373	9.398	9.423
31	9.449	9.474	9.500	9.525	9.550	9.576	9.601	9.627	9.652	9.677	9.703	9.728
32	9.754	9.779	9.804	9.830	9.855	9.881	9.906	9.931	9.957	9.982	10.008	10.033
33	10.058	10.084	10.109	10.135	10.160	10.185	10.211	10.236	10.262	10.287	10.312	10.338
34	10.363	10.389	10.414	10.439	10.465	10.490	10.516	10.541	10.566	10.592	10.617	10.643
35	10.668	10.693	10.719	10.744	10.770	10.795	10.820	10.846	10.871	10.897	10.922	10.947
36	10.973	10.998	11.024	11.049	11.074	11.100	11.125	11.151	11.176	11.201	11.227	11.252
37	11.278	11.303	11.328	11.354	11.379	11.405	11.430	11.455	11.481	11.506	11.532	11.557
38	11.582	11.608	11.633	11.659	11.684	11.709	11.735	11.760	11.786	11.811	11.836	11.862
39	11.887	11.913	11.938	11.963	11.989	12.014	12.040	12.065	12.090	12.116	12.141	12.167
40	12.192	12.217	12.243	12.268	12.294	12.319	12.344	12.370	12.395	12.421	12.446	12.471
41	12.497	12.522	12.548	12.573	12.598	12.624	12.649	12.675	12.700	12.725	12.751	12.776
42	12.802	12.827	12.852	12.878	12.903	12.929	12.954	12.979	13.005	13.030	13.056	13.081
43	13.106	13.132	13.157	13.183	13.208	13.233	13.259	13.284	13.310	13.335	13.360	13.386
44	13.411	13.437	13.462	13.487	13.513	13.538	13.564	13.589	13.614	13.640	13.665	13.691
45	13.716	13.741	13.767	13.792	13.818	13.843	13.868	13.894	13.919	13.945	13.970	13.995
46	14.021	14.046	14.072	14.097	14.122	14.148	14.173	14.199	14.224	14.249	14.275	14.300
47	14.326	14.351	14.376	14.402	14.427	14.453	14.478	14.503	14.529	14.554	14.580	14.605
48	14.630	14.656	14.681	14.707	14.732	14.757	14.783	14.808	14.834	14.859	14.884	14.910
49	14.935	14.961	14.986	15.011	15.037	15.062	15.088	15.113	15.138	15.164	15.189	15.215

Appendix

Appendix
Some Common Building Terms

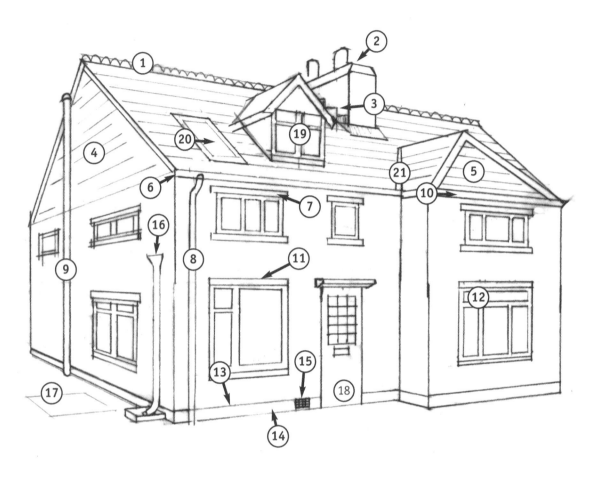

1	Ridge tiles	12	Top opening light
2	Flaunching	13	Damp-proof course 'DPC'
3	Stepped Flashing	14	'Blue brick' course
4	Gable end	15	Airbrick
5	Hipped roof	16	Hopper head
6	Eaves and fascia	17	Inspection chamber/manhole
7	Lintel	18	Threshold
8	Rainwater pipe 'RWP'	19	Dormer window
9	Soil vent pipe 'SVP'	20	Rooflight 'Velux'
10	Gutter	21	Valley
11	Soldier course at window head		

Recommended Reading

All About Selfbuild

Robert Mathews

Published by Blackberry Books

A comprehensive, highly detailed guide to self build.

ISBN 0 9515295 2 8

Boundary Disputes and How to Resolve Them

John Anstey

Published by RICS (Royal Institute of Chartered Surveyors)

Lots of practical tips on how to anticipate and resolve boundary disputes.

ISBN 0 85406 858 9

Build It Magazine

Published by Inside Communications Media Ltd

The oldest magazine for self builders, with lots of case studies and practical advice.

www.buildit-online.co.uk

Building Your Own Home

David Snell and Murray Armor

Ebury Press

One of the first books to tackle the subject comprehensively, this gives a thorough grounding in the whole process, from start to finish.

ISBN 0 09 188619 8

Concise DIY Guidebook to Project Management

Leonard Sales

Published by Construction Management Services 99 Ltd

Useful starting point for people planning to manage the construction work.

ISBN 0 9544768 0 8

Do It With an Architect

Barbara Weiss and Louis Hellman

Published by Mitchell Beazley

An excellent and humorous guide to getting the best out of your architect.

ISBN 1 84000 194 1

European House Now

Susan Doubilet and Daralice Boles

Published by Thames & Hudson

Good ideas on modern house design.

ISBN 0 500 28175 0

Recommended Reading

Getting the Builders In

Paul J. Grimaldi

Published by Elliot Right Way Plus

Advice on how to deal with builders, written by a builder.

ISBN 0 7160 3012 8

Grand Designs Magazine

Published by Media 10 Ltd

A tie-in with the Channel Four TV series.

Homebuilding and Renovating Magazine

Published by Ascent Publishing Ltd

A good quality publication that deals with all kinds of domestic building projects, including one-off houses.

www.homebuilding.co.uk

Houses in the Landscape

John and Jane Penoyre

Published by Faber & Faber

Illustrates the different characteristics of building methods in the regions of England and Wales.

ISBN 0 571 13287 1

How to Find and Buy a Building Plot

Roy Speer and Michael Dade

Published by Stonepound Books

ISBN 0 9533489 1 1

How to Get Planning Permission

Roy Speer and Michael Dade

Published by Stonepound Books

ISBN 0 9533489 2 X

Illustrated Handbook of Vernacular Architecture

R. W. Brunskill

Published by Faber and Faber

A good book for details of traditional building techniques for the different regions of England and Wales, with lots of illustrations.

ISBN 0 571 19503 2

Self Build and Design Magazine

Published by Waterways World Ltd

A good source of ideas, in design terms as well as more practical matters.

www.selfbuildanddesign.co.uk

Recommended Reading

The Home Plans Book

David Snell

Published by Ebury Press

The biggest collection of house plans available in the UK.

ISBN 0 09 186953 6

The Housebuilder's Bible

Mark Brinkley

Published by Ovolo Publishing Ltd

This covers many of the practical issues, with detailed and updated guidance on building costs.

ISBN 0 9524852 4 9

The New Natural House Book

David Pearson

Published by Conran Octopus Ltd

An excellent book for anyone interested in sustainable or 'green' building, and designing for healthy living.

ISBN 1 85029 985 4

The Whole House Book

Pat Borer and Cindy Harris

Published by the Centre for Alternative Technology Publications

Practical advice on how to make your house 'eco-friendly'.

ISBN 1 898-49 21 1

Timber Frame Construction

Wainwright and Keyworth

Published by the Timber Research and Development Association

Very detailed practical guide to the construction of timber-framed buildings.

ISBN 1 90051 032 4

Village Buildings of Britain

Matthew Rice

Published by Time Warner Books

A well-illustrated guide to traditional, vernacular buildings.

ISBN 0 316 72624 9

Working With Professionals

Edited by Andrew Pears

Published by Marshall Publishing

Advice on hiring and dealing with your building team.

ISBN 1 84028 221 5